LEONARDO'S MACHINES

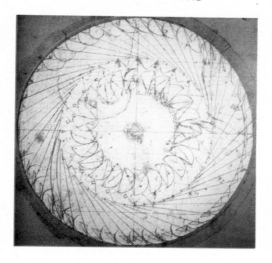

LEONARDO'S MACHINES

by Marco Cianchi

Introduction by Carlo Pedretti
Iconography by Alessandro Vezzosi
Translation by Lisa Goldenberg Stoppato

BECOCCI EDITORE

At a time of growing interest for Leonard's work; which coincides with the City of Vinci's efforts to remodel and enlarge its Museum, this publication like other studies and promotional activities under way in various Vincian centers (from Florence to Milan, from Amboise to Los Angeles), offers useful information to a wider range of readers. This book also seems to analyze correctly both the myth of Leonardo and the current interest in him while summing up the essential contribution of Da Vinci to Renaissance Science and technology. These results are obtained by means of a vast photographic documentation and the introduction of interpretative data. Therefore we would like to express our appreciation for this venture and for those responsibile for its completion.

Liliano Bartolesi
Mayor of Vinci

There are many people to thank now that this project is done: the Editor Saverio Becocci who entrusted me with this publication; the Mayor and the Clerk for Cultural Affairs of the City of Vinci for their interest; prof. Carlo Pedretti of the University of California at Los Angeles for his expert contribution of the original Introduction; Alessandro Vezzosi who handled the graphics and the illustrations and who helped revise the text. I also would like to thank the following people for their useful advice: prof. Paolo Galluzzi, ex-director of the Vinci Museum, prof. Di Pasquale of the Department of Architecture of the University of Florence (Institute of Construction), and Marta Romanelli, vice-director of the Museum and the Library of Vinci.

M.C.

Unnumbered illustrations:

On the front cover: illustration of geometric perspective, Cod. Atl. f. 263r.b; page one: sketch of a water-wheel, Cod. Atl. f. 258r.b; page two: "Leonardo's house" in Anchiano, the castle of Vinci which houses the Leonardo Museum, the Castle of Amboise, models of Leonardo's inventions in Clos-Lucé; page three (title page): model of a tank, Museum of Vinci (I.B.M.); on the back cover: sketch of a machine gun (detail), Cod. Atl. f.3r.a.

Photographs: Alessandro Vezzosi, the Leonardian Library of Vinci, the Archives "Tools-history of a territory" in Vinci.

The models which are illustrated belong to the collections of the Leonardo Museum of Vinci and of the National Museum of Science and Technology of Milan.

INTRODUCTION by Carlo Pedretti

The study of Vincian technology by means of models began rather recently — it is a phenomenon of the last fifty years. I believe that the first modern construction based on Leonardo's plans were the flying machines that Raffaele Giacomelli had Giuseppe Schneider make for the National Exposition of the History of Science, held in Florence in 1929 and for the International Exposition of Aeronautics held in London the same year. Those occasions revealed the didactic effectiveness of the Vincian models which, together with the interest itself, contributed to make the exhibitions entertaining as well as informative. The major exhibition on Leonardo held in Milan in 1939, with its important rooms of Da Vinci models, served as a launching-pad for an exploitation of Leonardo for chauvinistic and demagogical purposes. The exhibition was sent for propaganda reasons to America and to Japan where it was destroyed in a bombing. Leonardo's reputation was therefore saved by an act of war, or, so he would have called it by "beastly madness", which put an end to his use as a prophet of racial and expansionistic war ideologies.

After an important and long forgotten contribution of Kenneth Clark in 1935, the catalogue of his drawings at Windsor, research on Leonardo pratically ceased during the war. A rare exception, Popham's book on Leonardo's drawings, appeared in London in 1946, as if to declare the vitality and the validity of Clark's example. For the first time in a study of Leonardo's artistic works (aside from the national publications of his manuscripts and drawings) space was given to Vincian technology in a final chapter about his machines and architecture. These subjects are examined from selective and synthetic perspectives, from a cronological point of view which is tied to the stylistic development of the drawings, as well as from historical and documentary ones: a kind of visual commentary of the paragraphs of the famous letter [ill. II] that Leonardo sent to Lodovico Sforza when he was leaving for Milan in 1482 ca., the first real evidence of his claimed abilities in the field of civil and military engineering. Popham's analysis concentrates on the impressive drawing of an arsenal at Windsor Castle [fig. 25] in order to stress the most outstanding character of the early Vincian technological drawings — the sense of strength and of energy created by the presence of human figures at work. In fact Popham writes, «in fact the interest of the machine for raising cannon, which is illustrated, is subsidiary[1]; it is the mass of naked figures straining at the ropes and winches, the impression of energy conveyed by these toiling men, which makes this drawing an epitome of human effort». Therefore Popham was able to conclude that the Vincian military drawings of that period were generally livened by human figures caught in the act of using the machinery depicted: exhuberant, active and energetic figures. Thus one ends up prefering the drawings of machines so conceived to those without a human presence, like the « no doubt more valuable and interesting inventions», like the machine for cutting files on page 6r-b of the Codex Atlanticus [fig. 169], or in the numerous hydraulic devices, like the one Popham himself publishes as plate 297, an early sheet from the Codex Atlanticus, n. 386 r-b [fig. 66].

Popham, then was first person to show how to observe, understand and evaluate the Vincian technological drawings-not so much as divinations of future developments of technology (idea that should be forgotten), but rather as the expression of the leonardesque vision of the world at that time in its intense and complex ties with examples from classical antiquity re-proposed by the Scholastics and the Humanists (Biagio da Parma and Leon Battista Alberti), and then still used by the artisan and rural traditions that Leonardo constantly drew from, paying tacit homage to his native land. Observations on the relationship between Da Vinci's and Brunelleschi's technologies belong to recent years. I focalized on this subject in my recent publication, *Leonardo architetto* (Milan, 1978), while Franco Borsi and Bruno Zevi have also grasped the problem in all its implications. This is followed by an essay on « Leonardo and Territorial Interpretation» in a volume of miscellany about Lombardy, where I felt it was proper to emphasize the arsenal drawing. As Popham had already observed, our attention is concentrated on the efforts of a great crowd of workmen — as compact as phalanxes in battle formation — each intent on lifting a heavy piece of artillery onto a cart so that it can be moved to storage. It is a drawing whose subject could righfully be considered Lombard, while its explan atory nature seems to tie it to the type of drawing that would later be used to illustrate Cesariano's Vitruvio. And thus one almost doesn't notice at first glance that the scene is seen from above like a landscape in a perspective with several vanishing points, following the visual movement from the bottom to the top; and thus Leonardo

creates a sense of perspective acceleration which foreshadows that of the "Last Supper" [ill. I].
As in the "Last Supper", and moreover as in all of Leonardo's paintings or drawings, in his drawings of machines Leonardo manages to suggest movement, that is work effort, by means of the
drammatization of the space. In fact his machines are often placed either by allusion or by description, in their proper environment which usually means a landscope or a territorial view. Such
is the case in the drawing of a canal in order to demonstrate the use of two types of escavators
[figs. 48 and 49] — a traditional one which derives from Vitruvio and digs from the banks of the
canal, and the one that Leonardo invented which digs straight ahead on tracks laid in the canal
gradually as the escavation proceeds. And I do not understand why this important concept has
been overlooked in the recent construction built from these models. Leonardo's drawing, as it appears in the reconstruction of the sheet proposed in my book *Leonardo architetto* [fig. 262], is a
supreme example of a contestual drawing and is a demonstratively effective as the "explosive"
perspective also introduced by Leonardo in both his anatomical illustrations and his technological
plans, for example in the machine for cutting marble sketched in the Codex Atlanticus, f. Ir-c
[fig. 170].
On the other hand, the instruments used to illustrate a law of mechanics are often conceived ab-
stractly in neutral space with Leonardo seems to indicate with the close hatching in the background. These instruments and devices can be lined up in close casuistrial order like the pages of
the first of the Madrid manuscripts; elements of a technological language with Leonardo was
adding to with the same determination and insistence used in compiling his endless lists of words.
The principle of the compression of air, repeatedly noted and discussed by Leonardo especially in
the Leicester Codex, might be demonstrated with the traditional barber's pot of "pink water"
[for bloodletting] which Leonardo himself mentions and which may well have inspired him to
dream of a prolonged submersion in the water. The same principle is used in 1798 in the first submarine invented by the American Robert Fulton. Fulton also built a boat propelled according to
another principle already divined by Leonardo and explained in the Leicester Codex, the law of
the propulsive power of steam. In this case the model could be paired with those provided by
the theories of Huygens and Papin demonstrated in traditional physics laboratories.
Even the flying machine, all things considered can be placed in the same sphere of contextual
abstraction like the flyers that Goya draws in a night sky. And the reason why the model is hanging in thin air is not to simulate an unrealistic use conceived for it by Leonardo but rather to
submit it to an unlimited variety of points of view, thus giving it a structural and spatial rhythm

that almost suggests the hypnotic effect of Calder's mobiles.

Someday one hopes that we will reach a new conception of the Vincian museum, where models of his machines, presented with scientific accuracy based on the drawings which inspire them, will be used both to put Leonardo's contribution to technology in its proper historical focus and to shed light on the various aspects of an inventive ability which is constantly tied to a scenic and dynamic view of the world.

The remodelling and reorganization of the Leonardo Museum proposed by the City of Vinci with the help of various consultants coordinated by Alessandro Vezzosi, together with the various contributions of studies and of publications for divulgation, like this one edited by Marco Cianchi, show that we are already moving in the right direction.

Carlo Pedretti

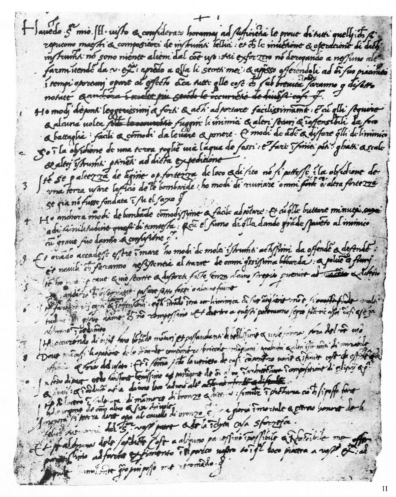

II

I. Leonardo, the "Last Supper", in S. Maria delle Grazie in Milan.

II. Letter to Ludovico il Moro, Cod. Atl. f. 391 r.-a, non autograph rough draft.

THE GREARS OF COSMOGONY

An intriguing theread winds its way through Leonardo's visual notes which through allegorical obscurity and technical revelations, through metaphors and symbolic forms, through mechanical intuitions and technological quotations and metal projections, crosses his cosmological research at suggestive levels, until it weaves a synthetic weft soaked in art and science, empiricism and philosophy, poetry and metaphysics... Although it's impossible to treat the subject thoroughly now, in any case it's worth illustrating this kind of a chessboard of singular iconographical topicality with a series of fragmentary images that provoke and sollecit a transversal reading. Instead of cristalizing it in conventional interpretative forms, he chooses for an ever more systematic mosaic the strangest and most contradictory tesserae, emblematic or indecipherable ones, following a vein of paradoxical references which from the fantastic world of medioeval archaisms reaches as far as the variously surreal or rational, trial or mysterious or conceptual ones of the artistic avant-gardes of this century, not by chance confronting itself with artists like Duchamp, Klee, Fuller, Jarry, Beuys... Leonardo's cosmic vision, already foreshadowed in his first drawing dated August 5, 1473 and almost biblically deflagratory, later, in his "deluges" (ill. III), takes form as anatomy and mechanics of the universe: Earth as a human body as a machine. «... The Earth has a spirit of growth: the flesh is the ground, the bones are the stratifications of rocks which form the mountains, the blood is the sping water...» In the image of the fetus in the uterus (ill. IV) we can read the cross-section of a planet or of a machine of life or of a flower, together with the analytic description of the details, perhaps confused with human and animal anatomy. The neck muscles (ill. XLV) almost seem to be musical strings, while next to the drawing, "stamped" with two skulls, is written: «Oh observer of this machine of ours, be not saddened by the fact that you make it known by means of the death of another, but instead take joy that our Creator has turned his intellect towards the excellence of such an instrument». In his inexhaustible research, Leonardo claims that the «painter must try to be universal... and disputes and competes with Nature and he is its Lord and God». And if it is true that his only science was that of the painter, then it seems even stranger, that Lomazzo says «Leonardo received from the sun the gift for forming all that human genius can ever speculate and imagine in the seven liberal arts...», considering that he certainly does not distinguish himself in the *Trivio*, and more than in the *Quadrivio* his final objective and his most personal expression of synthesis clearly were concentrated in painting as a "mental thing". His own "treatise" begins with the interrogative, «If painting is a science. Science is said to be that mental conversation...», certainly the painting of the "Adoration of the Magi" is already a "machine", like the "Battle of Anghiari" which also was to be considered his personal expression as a "poet of impetus". And the drawing is the key that the artist-scientist uses to penetrate into the world of phenomena: registration of knowledge, mirror for the experiencs of the world, troubling hieroglyph of the mysteries of the machine of nature revealed and reorganized in functional forms and artificial machines, finally precious, lyrical and instinctively esthetic processing of the data of reality. His own ideal autobiography notes the polemic cues tied to an environment where both the contradictions intrinsic to his thought and the extrinsic ones of Leonardo's public image (the controversies, for example, about magic, alchemy, invention, imitation...) become exasperated; thus he accuses, in the passage about the "men without letters", the "foolish people who, swollen and pompous, dress and adorn themselves not with their own labours, but with those of others; and will not concede me my own; and if I am to be scorned as an inventor, then much more than I, they, trumpeters and actors of other people's works should be criticized». Museums for the machines of Leonardo, even though modern, often present a limited interpretation and an anacronistic image both on the esthetic and didactic levels, and certainly do not

III

IX

IV

X

V

XI

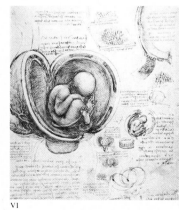

VI

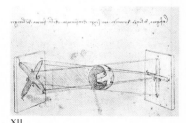

XII

VII

VIII

XIII

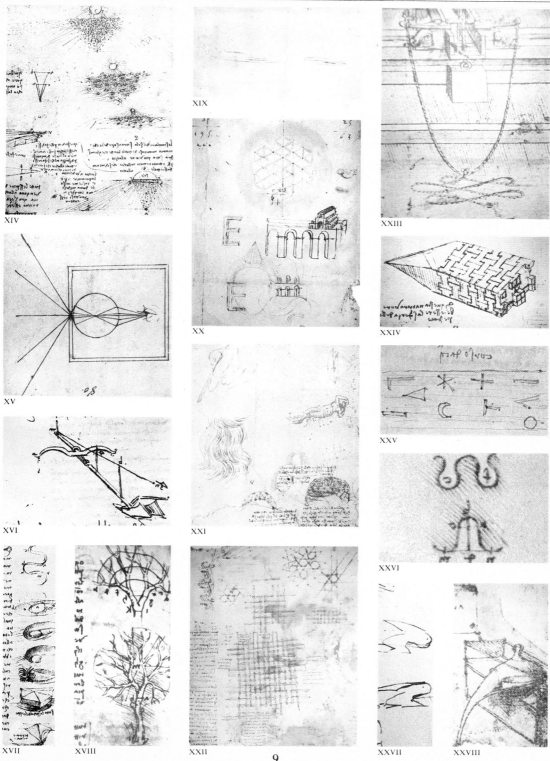

XIV

XIX

XXIII

XV

XX

XXIV

XVI

XXI

XXV

XVII

XVIII

XXII

XXVI

XXVII

XXVIII

XXIX

XXXIII

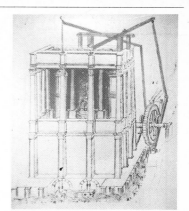

XIL

XXX

XXXIV

XL

XXXV

XXXVI

XLI

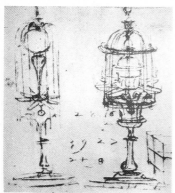

XXXI

XXXVII

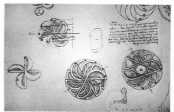

XLII

XXXII

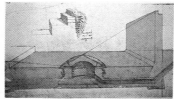

XXXVIII

XLIII

10

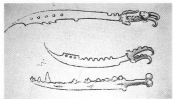

XLIV

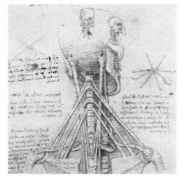

XLV

XLVI

XLVII

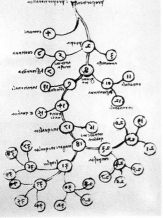

XLVIII

take full advantage of the possibilities offered by the theme of the model or of the environment or of the scenography or of the comparison. For this problem there are many possible directions to follow from contriving a complex machine for the the exhibition of gadgets and curtailing the retoric of the myth in order to focus, using up to date techniques and new means, on the true meaning which is also the most important one both historically and topically; to analyzing the details and creating a "poetry of the fragment" interested in the elements of machinery in a philological sense, or else comparing esthetically and symbolically the "gears of cosmogony" spread throughout the pages and the margins of the codices with various iconologies. These "gears" are the following: the emblem "destinato rigore" with solar energy and hydraulic power for the machine which is a compass-rudder and a wheel-sweep net (ill. IV), compared to the allegory of government (Windsor n. 12496) and F. 191r. of the Codex Atl. which «shows how Earth is surrounded and clothed by its provinces»; the comparison of the dynamic lines in the flight through the wind and the billows (ill. V) and in the whirlpools of water (fig. 41); the «body created by the perspective of L. da V., student of experience... made without the model of anybody, only using simple lines» (ill. VII); the sundial of «sol per te le mie ore son generate» (VIII); the perspective machine (IX) and the painter's studio (XIII) and the room of mirrors (X); the «way to weigh air and to know when the weather will change» amid nude figures in animated conversations (XI); studies of shadows and glances (ill. XII e XV), with references to a projector and a dark room (fig. 174); the plow capable of furrowing «straight for many miles» (XVI) and the unexplainable «way of ploughing without oxen» (C. Atl. 26 r.a.); the «simulacra of the sun on the waves» like nets covered with stars (XIV); the "figures" of the erosion of the banks of rivers (XVII); the "rational" structure of the trees (XVIII); the anamorphic shapes (XIX); the composite sheets: the "left hand" with Ariadne and sketches ofcenterings (XXI) and the prints of lunules with a Medici ring and architectural letters (XX); the frequent varieties of knots and braids and textures: in the sketches of wooden covers (XXII), in the end of a rope of a machine for battle (XXIII), in the joints of a wedge (XXIV), in the chains (XXXV), in the marquetry (Oxford) or in the emblematic pages of "Academia" (in the Ambrosiana), in the scaffolding, in the barriers or even in the bird cage ("Thoughts turn to hope", C. Atl. 68v.); the hieroglyphics of a poetic alphabet (XXV); the male/female symbolism of a gear (XXVI); the dynamic essentiality of the purist abstractions in the drawing of a wing (XXVII) or of a «potential "straightness"» which runs between the center of a suspended weight and the center of the world» (Cod. Atl. 118v.b); the suggestive stills with anthropomorphic and magical shapes (XXVIII); the aerial equilibrium of a globe and of a "kite-glider" (XXIX); the dynamic, almost futuristic, lines of the trajectory of flight (XXX); the architectural model in a movable fountain (XXXI); the naval architectural plans with details of an archaism close to proto-design (XXXII); the mausoleum derived from an Etruscan tomb with a circular plan and six arms (XXXIII); the notes on the sheets of Francesco di Giorgio's treatise with human proportions inscribed in capitals and columns (XXXIV); a man and a woman attached to a spiral column (XXXVI); the allegory of Virtue who blinds Vice who has a scorpions's tail, the tongue of a snake and a mask (XXXVII); the metaphysic plasticity of the military architecture (XXXVIII); buildings like hydraulic machines with ornate capitals and classicizing forms (XXXIX); architectural structures modeled after the abstract patterns of a cogwheel (XL); archaic weapons similar to voracious fruit (XLI) or that derive from animal forms (XLIV); rotating helices or explosive shells between archers in harmonic motion (XLII, XLIII); musical instruments derived from imaginary beasts (XLVI); the diagram of how sound fades away, perhaps on contact with the smell of flowers (XLVII); the genealogical tree of the proportions of drawing (XLVIII); spiral shaped, vortical and synthetic

XLIX

L   LI

LII

LIII

LIV

movements (IL, L, LI, LII); the helmet-mask (LIII); oven-flower (C. Atl. 396r.); a "steam blower" (LIV) conceived as the metal bust of a boy; automatons like the «bird of the comedy» (fig. 160) and the stage prop of a revolving mountain (fig. 161) and the references to Heron of Alexandra or Apollordorus of Damascus, to Giacomo Fontana or to Valturio; finally, the face-mask of a robot

Alessandro Vezzosi

LEONARDO AND MACHINES

The inventions

The myth that Leonardo was an ingeniuous forerunner of all the discoveries and inventions of our era springs from the mysterious figure himself and, understandably, from the initial spontaneous considerations of he who sees his technological drawings or the models of his machines. The propaganda of the "Italian genius", begun with the Leonardo exhibition in Milan in 1939, later contributed decisively to that myth, together with a more recent packaging of a commercial image for the greater public that has clearly been a success.

To tell the truth it is not possible to say that all of the machines and inventions of Leonardo were produced by his original and prolific genius; to convince ourselves to that effect we need only read words written by Roger Bacon in mid XIII century far away in England: «... it's possible to build vessels for navigating without oarsmen so that very big river and maritime boats can travel guided by a solitary helmsman much more swiftly than they would if they were full of men. It's also possible to build wagons which move without horses by means of a miraculous force. And I think that the reaping chariots that the ancients used in battle must have been made like this. It's also possible to construct machines for flight built so that a man in the middle of one can manoeuver it using some kind of device that makes the specially built wings beat the air the way birds do when they fly. And similarly it's also possible to build a small winch capable of raising and lowering infinitely heavy weights... it's also possible to build devices for walking on seas and rivers and for touching their bottoms withou taking any risks. And Alexander the Great doubtlessly used these instruments to explore the ocean floor as the astronomer Etico narrates. In fact there is no doubt that such instruments had already been built in ancient times and are still being built today, except for the flying machine that neither I nor anyone I know have ever seen. However, I do know a scholar who tried to build this instrument as well. It's possible to build almost an infinite number of bridges, for example, which can be stretched across rivers without using any kind of pillars or supports, and of unheard of machines and inventions».

All of the machines, all of the "inventions" considered to be Leonardo's are described here one by one as things which belong to a centuries old tradition that was still alive and active in the second half of the fourteen hundreds in engineers like Taccola, Buonaccorso Ghiberti and Francesco di Giorgio Martini, following in the tracks of the recent brunelleschian tradition. The military treatises, the miscellanies of technical and mechanical information that these writers drafted accompanied by effective if often rough illustrations, were in great demand and were copied and studied by Leonardo as some of his notes and memoirs show. There were certainly more of such works available in Leonardo's lifetime than we know today.

Thus we must realize, once and for all that Leonardo's technological drawings often draw from other writers' books and manuscripts and even more frequently from the observation of the activities of the workshops or from the exchange of ideas with scholars and technicians of his era. We must come to the conclusion that, while his mechanics and engineering are, for their breadth and depth of experience, unique and at times ahead of their times, they are not fruit ripened all alone in a desert.

The sources

There are thousands of drawings of machines by Leonardo grouped in various codices in France, England, Spain and Italy which are believed to be only a fourth of the Da Vinci corpus, the rest of which has been lost. And we don't even know for sure whether Leonardo's machine actually got built, since the historic sources are of little help, insisting primarily on the whims of his mind which was always ready to invent new and marvelous objects without saying a word about their actual construction (excluding a few exceptions, for example his stage sets).

At the time of his death in France in 1519, Leonardo left all of his manuscripts to his faithful companion Francesco Melzi who guarded them carefully and devotedly all his life; the same is not true of his son Orazio who is responsible for the first dispersion of such precious material that was, however, soon recovered by Pompeo Leoni, the sculptor of the court of Spain and a great collector of works of art. He reorganized it using scissors and glue in the intent of better organi-

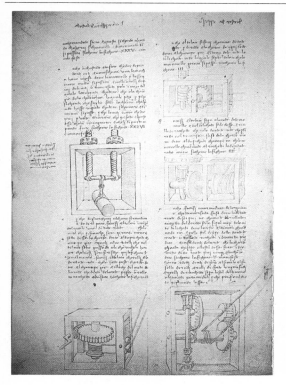

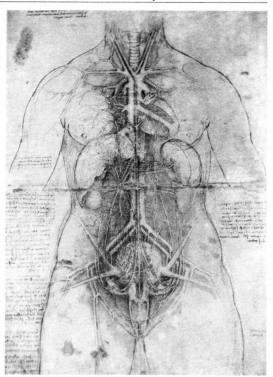

LVI. Francesco di Giorgio Martini, page of the Ash. cod. 361 of the Medi-
ceo-Laurenzian Library in Florence (with notes by Leonardo)

LVII. Leonardo, anatomical drawing, R.L. of Windsor n. 12281r.

zing the immense number of pages in more sturdily bound codices, each with different dimensions and subjects.

Thus the "Codex Atlanticus" was born — probably given such a name, which derives from the Greek work "Atlas", because of its large format — which should be considered the fundamental text in any study of Vincian technology. It is made of 1200 sheets (reduced by Leoni to 400) with technical and scientific drawings which are grouped together without any precise logical or chronological order and which belong to different periods of Leonardo's life, ranging from his youth to the last years of his life. When Leoni died in 1608 the Codex Atlanticus, after passing through many hands, came into the possession of Count Arconati who gave it to the Ambrosian Library in Milan in 1636. It was taken away from there with the authorization of a Napoleonic writ and was transferred to the National Library in Paris, only to be returned in 1815 to the "Ambrosiana" where it can be found today.

Arconati had given, along with the "Codex Atlanticus", others labeled with the letters of the alphabet from A to M, which on the authorization of the same Napoleonic writ, were taken to the Institute of France and never returned. The most important one on the subject in question, the "B Manuscript" (which can be dated roughly in 1488) includes many pages of drawings with machines for battle, boats, bridges and flyings with machines for battle, boats, bridges and flying with machines for battle, boats, bridges and flying machines. But there are others of the twelve manuscripts in the Institute of France which contain interesting technological drawings. The same is true for the "Arundel Codex" and a few sheets of the collection at Windsor which reached England after complex and often obscure vicissitudes.

Particularly worthy of note, for the specific nature of its subject, is the small codex about the "Flight of Birds" written around 1505 which, after being stolen from the Institute of France, found its way to the Royal Library in Turin, where it can be found today.

The most recent discovery (1967) is that of two manuscripts in the National Library of Madrid, which bear the numbers 8936 and 8937, but generally are called Madrid I and Madrid II. The first one, written between 1493 and 1497, is the more surprising of the two, not only for its considerable contribution towards a fuller understanding of Leonardo's technological works, but also for its beauty which seems gelid as compared to the quick sketches in the other codices. Its drawings neatly illustrate machines and mechanical parts, pieces of clock-work and various tools. The intent of such an orderly and precise treatment was clearly comunicative: probably the "summa" of a long and agitated period of research.

The complex vicissitudes of the codices — lost, dismembered, then reunited in an arbitrary manner and in the end lost for long periods of time in private collections or on dusty library shelves — are partly responsible for the chronological chaos that recent philology is creating. But it must be taken into consideration that a true chronology probaby never existed due to the nature of the pages themselves which are filled with thoughts and notes mixed with drawings of machines and observations made in workshops or taken from other books and which were often used by Leonardo on several occasions distant in time as happens normally in a notebook.

Since it's difficult to organize the material chronologically and because it's necessary to offer the layman a clear and well organized view, we have decided to group the drawings by subject, following a system of classification that has become standard: battle machines, hydraulic ones, flying ones and last of all a chapter entitled "Leonardo's mechanics" which includes all the mechanical parts and all the gadgets and the tools that can not be included in one of the first three categories because of their heterogenousness. Each machine is explained by a catalogue entry and occasionally there is a photograph of the model built from the original drawing. Each chapter has an introduction on the specific subject and is subdivided by subtitles which serve to organize the material more thoroughly.

The itinerary

While still adolescent Leonardo arrived from the countryside of Vinci in the workshop of Verrocchio, perhaps the most prominent and certainly the most successful one in fifteenth century Florence. The apprenticeship of a lad in a workshop was based on daily practise and constant contact with the materials and the techniques of the field; this, however, was completed by lessons in rudimentary mathematics, and grammar and especially by the constant practise in the art of drawing which, considering of its visual immediacy, was often used in place of words to explain projects, to discuss solutions and to convince others of one's logic. And Leonardo certainly made good use of these lessons to which he added daily conversations with artisans in their workshops and at their construction sites, as well as avid reading of the technical treatises that contemporary engineers wrote often on the basis of the ancient texts rediscovered by the humanists.

It was Brunelleschi who, inspired by the classical texts, relaunched the dignity of manual activity, earning enthusiastic reactions both from artisans and from men of culture like Leon Battista Alberti who saw in such an attitude towards labor the foundations for his "città terrena". The cupola of Santa Maria del Fiore — miraculously erected above the Florentine skyline — was a kind of beacon for the artists who found the starting point and the reason for similar projects in the innovative aspects of such an undertaking. According to Vasari, Leonardo «... each day made models and drawings for flattening mountains and for tunneling through them in order to pass from one plain to another and he showed how to lift and pull heavy weight using levers, winches and screws... and among these models and drawings there was one in which he showed the numerous clever citizens who then ruled Florence several ways to raise the temple of S. Giovanni in Florence and put stairs under it without ruining it; and his reasoning was so convincing that it seemed feasible even though after his departure everyone soon realized how impossible such an undertaking was».

For those who know Brunelleschi's biography the relationship between Leonardo's interests and the ingenious machines built by Brunelleschi to hoist the construction materials up to the level of the cupola is quite clear — in fact recent studies have proved a direct dependence —; so is the similarity between Leonardo's display of genius in his plans to raise the Baptistry and the other

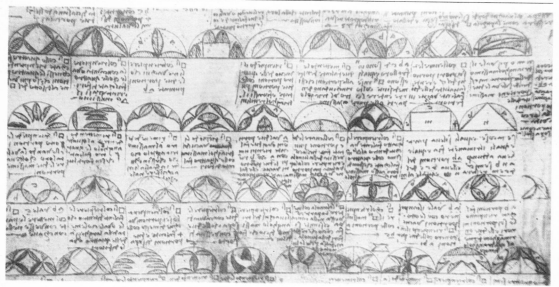

LVIII. Leonardo, Lunules, Cod. Atl. f. 167r.a-b

"incredible", yet successful project for the cupola which was initially received with similar incredulity and scepticism. But Leonardo seems to take pleasure in the wonder produced by the ingenious machines and in the creation of a public image of himself as a sorcerer, image probably added to by the fascination for esoteric themes in Florence at that time.

At age thirty - «... having now sufficiently seen and considered the proofs of all those who count themselves masters and inventors of instruments of war», but knowing that even in peacetime he can «... give perfect satisfaction and to the equal of any other in architecture and the composition of buildings public and private, and in conduiting water from one place to another» and, what's more, knowing he can sculpt and paint «as well as anyone else, no matter who he is» and, finally, promising to cast a bronze horse that «will be the immortal glory and the eternal honor of the Sforza house» — at age thirty, as we were saying, Leonardo feels that there is little more to be learned in Florence and that he is ready to make the move to Milan where he is received at the court of Ludovico il Moro. The cultural environment in Milan where Leonardo settled, starting in 1482, for roughly twenty years, is quite different from the one in Florence. There is a concrete and pragmatic attitude far more pronounced than in Florence: there is less lingering over the beautiful forms, words and images that hide the secrets of the universe, instead all activity is motivated by a logical and physical culture which has its most vital centers in northern Italy and in other European countries near by. In addition the court which Leonardo frequents reflects the interests of a nonintellectual but curious Lord who was more of a soldier than a man of letters, who loved feasts and amusements, but whose primary preoccupation was the economic and military strength of his state. Leonardo was sought out and appreciated in particular as an artist who represented the refined culture of Florence but also had to resolve or at least simply to deal with the numerous practical problems that constantly arose in a large State and in a lively court like the one in Milan. Frequenting workshops gave him the chance to deepen and to enlarge his knowledge of various techniques; and he also studied physics and mechanics from the works of the major classic authors. The most important of these for Leonardo was Archimedes because of his constant recourse to experience and mathematics.

In this period Leonardo fills his codices with gears and cogwheels, with ingenious solutions for hydraulic problems and with splendid mechanical inventions for flight, with cannons, and contrivances for weaving, with clock mechanisms and studies of human anatomy: some of these are notes from other authors' works, others are quick sketches made in a workshop, others are ideas

15

barely delineated or attempts to improve existing implements or recently invented machinery. They are, in any case, not only, the product of a period of great, almost furious activity concentrated in the practical vein suggested by the milieu, but also represent the flowering of old dreams cultivated with love, like that of the flying machine. All this gets translated into the dynamic graphics of each drawing which is a project, a discussion, a verification and a work of art all rolled into one.

However, 1496 marks a sharp change in the course of Leonardo's activities. This is the date of the start of his friendship with the Franciscan monk Luca Pacioli who, frequenting the same court in Milano, inspired Leonardo's interest for mathematics and, especially for geometry by studying Euclid. Leonardo's interest in mathematics is not, in itself, a novelty since it forms the basis of perspective, the painter's science whose laws were taught in Renaissance workshops; but his particularly intense concentration on the subject for a period of about eight years is entirely new. According to the sources he lost most of his practical interests in this period.

The result of such an assiduous experience was to be a kind of superior consciousness, a deeper and more intimate understanding of the Universe, also definitely contributed to by his recent study of human anatomy which revealed the extraordinary relationships between micro and macrocosm. And all of his later activity seems to show traces of these fundamental experiences: in the pagination of some of the codices one notes the need to express and sum up the long and agitated experience of genius freneticly applied to study. The geographic elevations and the city maps become more frequent, the sheets are covered by the equal and fascinating decomposition of lunules — changeable forms of the same geometric reality — Nature is probed more deeply in the studies of hydraulics and aerology. The machines become rarer and almost disappear or else, as in the paradigmatic case of the flying machine, end up collaborating with Nature itself.

The "infinite reasons"

Leonardo imagines the world as a giant machine set in motion by spiritual forces and controlled in its perfect mechanisms by a superior intelligence that has arranged everything according to mathematical laws. Leonardo is not interested in spiritual phenomena (which he leaves to the monks and the philosphers) but rather in natural ones that can be approached, studied and analyzed through tangible experience. For him it's possible to reach an understanding of the "infinite reasons" of the Universe, the mechanisms of the great machine of nature, only through experience, which, together with mathematics, is the mother of all certainly. Observing the flight of a bird, anatomizing a human body, he realizes not only that all things are tied together by an infinite number of threads but also that everything has a mechanical and automatic nature. Man is a machine, a bird is a machine; the whole Universe is a machine. The movement of an arm, of a leg, the movement of a wing are all regulated by precise mechanical and mathematical-laws which Leonardo reproduced, once he had understood them, in his artificial machines built from levers, gears and other devices. Thus his works are organic and at the same time compete with Nature: organic because they spring from the same "reasons" used by Nature, and competitive because these machines are produced by human genius vying with Nature in the attempt to populate the world with creations. And since the world is a living organism, then even machines must be considered "living" things — at this point Leonardo's reasoning reflects the platonic theses absorbed by him when he was young — because man, like God who in the beginning set the great machine of the Universe in motion, gives inert mechanisms and cold gears a "Spiritual force" which animates them as "if they were alive".

Art and science

The word "machine", in ancient times tied to the concept of "genius", thus takes on a much broader meaning than in its current use (for example "machines" are not only those implements used by man in his work, but also stage sets, weapons, instruments as well as hydraulic and architectural constructions, automatons and clock mechanisms), including even Leonardo's strictly artistic activities. Once it has been decided that "imitation" means creation and that it requires an understanding of Nature, then painting and poetry — which according to Leonardo "imitate Nature as much as their capabilities will let them" — like machinery are products of experience and of human genius which reproduce Nature's miracle. How else can the "Last Supper" be defined if not as a "machine" based on mathematics (its perspective) and set in motion from the center by Christ's gesture which activates the gears of the feelings and of the reactions of the Apostoles?

Thus we can abolish barrier between Leonardo's scientific and artistic activities which actually prove to be closely linked and equally indebted to one another. In fact if his art makes use of his scientific research and of the automatisms that characterize his machines, then these in turn depend on his artistic capacity to captivate the pulsating essence in order to understand the animation which characterizes the Universe.

Marco Cianchi

MACHINES FOR WAR

A noble warrior tradition had been passed down from antiquity by means of treatises and through the experiences of men of arms. For example in the tenth century the military works of the ancient Greeks were well known thanks to Hero from Byzantium; and later the Middle Ages filtered the lessons of the ancient Romans for use by knights and crusaders as is shown in Guido da Vigevano's treatise on military "machines" which dates from the first half of the thirteen hundreds.

Putting aside the rest of Europe, although it too is full of useful examples, in order to follow the tradition in Renaissance Italy, we find at first a generation of engineers, inventors and builders of military "machines" like Taccola, Valturio and Francesco di Giorgio Martini, which finds itself at the crossroads between a rich past and a present in turmoil beyond which laid Leonardo.

Since the control of the political situation in Italy depended increasingly on military might, its rulers vied for the help of such battle specialists both for defensive and offensive objectives, and military treatises were in great demand as well.

1

Even Leonardo decided to insist on his skills in the field of military engineering when seeking employment at the court ol Ludovico il Moro in the following very famous letter. We include only the part which refers to battle "machines":

1. *I know how to build very light strong bridges, made to be easily transported, so as to follow and at times escape from the enemy, as well as others which are safe from damage by fire and from battle wear, easy and convenient to take apart and build. And I know how to burn and destroy the enemy's ones.*
2. *I know techniques useful in invading a territory like how to drain the water out of moats and how to make an infinite number of bridges and covered walk-ways and ladders other machines useful for such expeditions.*
3. *Item, if in the course of an offensive the height of an embankment or the strength of site should preclude shelling, I*

know techniques for destroying any fortress or other stronghold not built on solid rock.

4. *I also know how to built cannons which are easy to move, that can shoot a storm of small stones and create smoke which heartily frightens the enemy, creating great damage and confusion.*
5. *And in case one is at sea, I know of many instruments suitable both for offensive and defensive maneuvers and of ships that will resist the biggest shells, gunpowder and smoke.*
6. *Item, I know how to reach certain designated sites by means of tunnels and secret and winding passages if it is necessary to cross moats and rivers.*
7. *Item, I will build covered wagons which are so safe and unattackable that no matter how big a multitude of soldiers is, they will still be frightened into breaking ranks at the sight of them in middle of the enemy artillery. And the infantry can follow them in great numbers, unharmed without meeting any resistance.*
8. *Item, if necessary, I will build unusual bombards, mortars and light ordnance with beautiful and useful shapes.*
9. *Whenever the shelling fails, I will invent catapults, mangonels, traps and other unusual and marvelous instruments; and in short for each situation I will build a variety and an infinite number of things for defending and for attacking...*

Written in Florence when he was thirty, the letter shows young Leonardo's assiduous interest in battle techniques and tools which he often borrows from ancient or contemporary treatises. His interest is so broad and varied that his twenty year stay in Milan resulted in important innovations in the development of firearms whose appearance on the battle field radically changed the techniques of fortification and of assault.

Leonardo worked out a way to make the still quite rudimentary cannons and bombards more efficient: he studied their casting, their loading, their lighting and their cooling and increased their capacities and their speed of fire. And he was also interested in the shape and the trajectory of the shot so that the could increase the precision of each shot: from experiments with jets of water he deduced a parabolic curve which foreshadowed, with luckly insight, the studies of the principle of inertia by Galileo and Newton.

After the long period of activity in Milan under Ludovico il Moro's patronage, Leonardo became so famous that in 1502 Cesare Borgia decided to hire him as an architect and a military engineer.

2

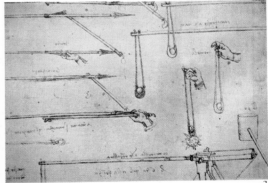

3

1. RAPID FIRE CROSSBOW Cod. Alt. f.387r.

The crossbow is one of the traditional battle "machines" that Leonardo tries to modernize by increasing either the strength or the speed of fire, as in this case. The archer, seated in the middle of the large wheels only has to release the arrow after having aimed through the sight. The loading of the four crossbows is an automatic consequence of the movement of the wheel to which they are attached. This is turned by a group of "walkers" protected by a wooden shield. The crossbows arrive already loaded one at a time in front of the archer and are always ready for use, thus considerably increasing the speed and the danger of the weapon.

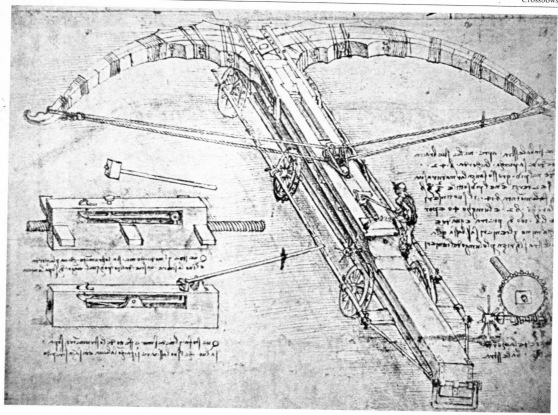

4

2. WHEEL FOR LOADING CROSSBOWS
Cod. Atl. f. 64v.-b

In this drawing Leonardo shows us another rapid fire crossbow, essentially like the last one but with more bows and almost completely automatized. In fact it requires only one man to work the crank mechanism sketched to the right, which both turns the wheel and loads the crossbows one after another by means of a releasing device connected to the shaft.

3. SLINGSHOT AND DARTS Cod. Atl. f. 51 v.-a.

Sketches of traditional weapons in an elegant graphic context.

4. GIANT CROSSBOW Cod. Atl. f.53v.-ab.

Leonardo himself tells us what the dimensions of this enormous crossbow are: it "opens its arms, meaning where one stretches its strings, 42 armlengths" (roughly 24 m.) and is moun-

ted on a cart "2 armlengths wide and 40 long". The figure of the archer gives us an idea of the proportions. The gigantic bow was supposed to be built from laminated sectins so as to increase its flexibility and strength. The bow string is pulled by a screw mechanism which is shown in the detail study at lower right. The release mechanism is illustrated in its percussion and lever versions by the two devices drawn to the left. The wheels tilt in order to guarantee a stabile base for shooting.

5

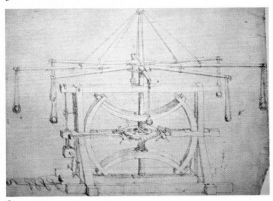

6

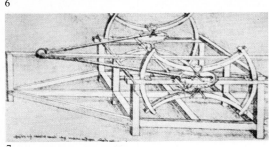

7

8

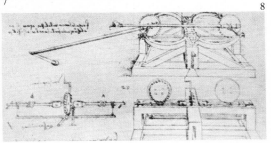

5. **CATAPULT WITH A WINCH Cod. Atl. f.51r.**
6. **CENTRIFUGE WITH MULTIPLE SLINGSHOTS**
   Cod. Atl. f.57r.-b.
7. **MACHINE FOR THROWING STONES AND BOMBS**
   Cod. Atl. f.51v.-b.
8. **CATAPULT AND CROSSBOW Cod. Atl. f.54v.-a**
9. **SERIES OF CATAPULTS Cod. Atl. 50v.-ab.**

The catapult is surely one of the oldest of the traditional weapons. Leonardo shows interest more than once in these out-of-date battle tools which fill page ofter page of the Codex Atlanticus. An extraordinarily beautiful and varied page appears in the full page illustration where the inventions are backed up by an extreme clarity of drawing and by a superb sense of impagination. Leonardo seems more interested in the elasticity of the shapes than in the possibility of actually using machines; yet on certain occasions these might well have been more threatening than the still rudimentary firearms. For example note che interesting catapult (fig. 5) which has a flexible arm bent backwards by a man-powered winch as well as a spoon reachable by ladder previously loaded with the stone to be flung. The winch has a catch which unhooked releases the flexible arm which in turn hits the spoon throwing the stone quite a distance. A series of similar catapults used simultanously would have provided excellent defence against approaching troops. There is also another ingenious invention, the multiple slingshot which uses the centrifugal force generated by the sudden release of energy built up in the crossbows (previously loaded by winches on a screw shaft). The loaded slingshots, rapidly set in rotation, will go from a vertical to a horizontal position and thus will sling their shot.

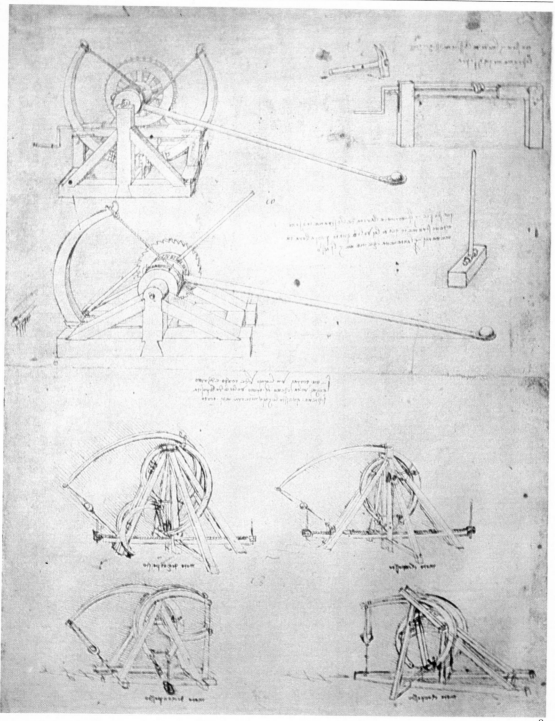

10

10.-11. REAPING WAGONS AND TANK
Turin, ex-Royal Library
and British Museum B.B. 1030

The idea of a covered wagon able to penetrate the enemy lines and followed by soldiers had already emerged in the Middle Ages and had been enthusiastically taken up in the fourteen hundreds. Leonardo designed a heavy wagon shaped like a tortoise armed with cannons on all sides and perhaps reinforced with metal plates (fig. 11). According to Leonardo the problem of how to move it, which others had hoped to solve with sails, could be resolved by eight men inside it working a set of gears connected to the wheels. He had even thought of using horses in place of the men but the risk that the animals might panic in such a tight and noisy space soon dissuaded him.

Another type of wagon, in this case equipped with scythes, which already existed in ancient Roman times, is mentioned by Leonardo: « *These wagons were of various types and often did as much damage to the allies as to the enemies... against these wagons archers, men with slingshots, throwers and shooters, all*

kinds of darts, lances, stones, fire, drumrolls and shouts must be used... and these will frighten the horses which unbridled will bolt in spite of their drivers... » Leonardo's drawing (fig. 10) shows a similar type of wagon pulled by horses with rotating scythes set in motion by an ingenious drive mechanism which is connected by means of a shaft to a system with "cog wheels and lantern rochets" that is directly linked to the movement of the wagon's wheels.

12. DEVICE FOR PUSHING AWAY ASSAULT LADDERS
Cod. Alt. f.49v.-b

13. REAPING PROPELLER BLADES FOR FELLING ASSAILANTS
Cod. Atl. f.32v.-a

14. DEFENCE OF RAMPARTS WITH BOMBARDS
Windsor B.R. n. 12275

Leonardo worked out many defense systems with simple yet effective inventiveness. For example: if the assailants tried to lean ladders against walls in order to climb them, they could be pushed away with a long rod hidden

11

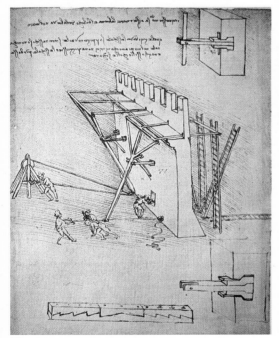

12

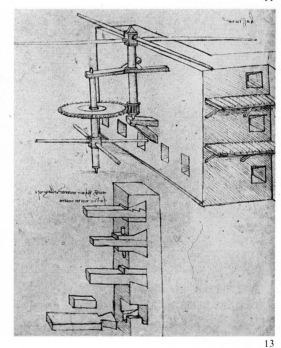

13

14

in the wall which could be put into use by a lever pulled from within. The drawing (fig. 12) itself speaks more clearly than any explanation. In case the assailants reached the top of the wall they could be repelled by rotating blades which could mow down anyone within range (fig. 13). With greater concessions to invention and to esthetics (see fig. 14) one might imagine a series of bombards in a row which simultaneously would shoot shells and projectiles beyond the bastions to be defended.

15

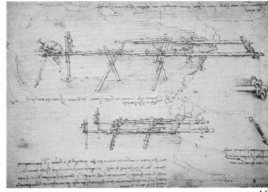

16

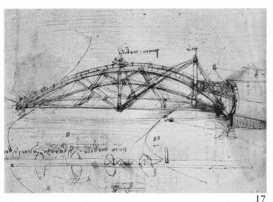

17

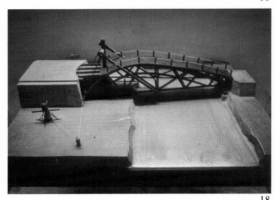

18

15. ARCHED BRIDGE Cod. Atl. f.22r.
16. EXTENSION BRIDGE Cod. Atl. f.16v.
17. TRESTLE BRIDGE Cod. Atl. f.312 r.-a.
18. MODEL OF A TRESTLE BRIDGE
(see fig. 17), Museum of Milan

These are the "light and strong bridges" that Leonardo promised in his letter to "il Moro". They can be built rapidly with materials that are easy to find and to transport (small tree trunks and strong ropes) and are meant primarily for military purposes. Since they facilitate crossing rivers, they permit rapid and unexpected troop movements, thus contributing to the surprise factor which is often fundamental for the success of a battle (figs. 15 and 16). These bridges use the laws of statics and of material resistence which Leonardo had developed while pursuing architectural interests. The plan for a swinging bridge (fig. 17) is also intended for military use. Leonardo conceived it with a single span attached to one bank by means of a vertical hinge on which it rotates. It can be moved by ropes and winches while

wheels and metal rollers make sliding it possible. It also has a caisson as a counterweight which helps its balance and facilitates tre manoeuvre while the bridge is suspended in mid-air before reaching the other bank.

19. MOVABLE LADDERS Cod. Forster I, f.46v.
20. ASSAULT LADDERS Cod. Atl. f.316v.
21. ASSAULT TECHNIQUES Ms. B f.59v.
22. COVERED CART FOR ATTACKING
FORTIFICATIONS Cod. Atl. f.391 v.-a.

Leonardo devised techniques for assault as well as for defence and drew many types of rope ladders that can be carried easily to the foot of the walls. A whole series of examples appears in the drawing in fig. 20, while in fig. 21 we see a man climbing a wall using "alpine" techniques, by driving spikes into the wall to be scaled. The movable assault ladder is quite interesting: it is made from units that can be taken apart and is linked to a "cog wheel-screw" mechanism which lengthens, shortens,

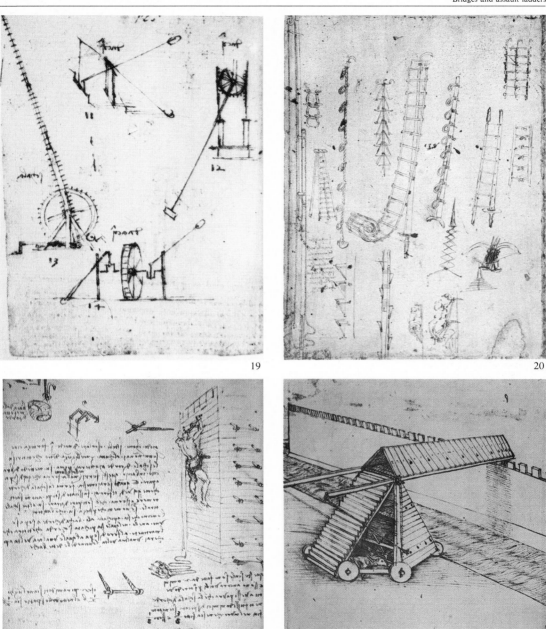

19

20

21

22

raises and lowers the ladder. Thus it can be used on any site and it is very difficult for the defenders to ward it off. Leonardo also borrows a covered ladder with a movable base with wheels from antiquity. It is illustrated in the drawing in fig. 22. Once the appropriate distance from the wall has been reached a footbridge with a peaked roof can be lowered with the help of ropes into place on the fortress walls, so that the soldiers can reach the enemy's defence positions unharmed.

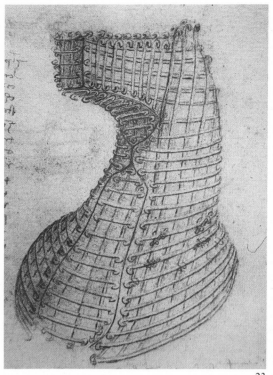

23

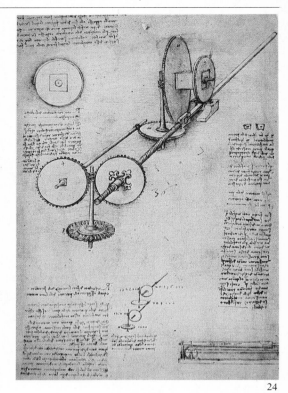

24

**23. PLAN FOR CASTING
THE SFORZA MONUMENT**
Cod. Madrid II, f.157r.

24. MACHINE FOR PROFILING CANNON PARTS
Cod. Atl. f.2r.

25. THE FOUNDRY Windsor B.R. n. 12647

While working in Verrocchio's workshop, Leonardo must have encountered casting problems, but once he reached Milan his interest in the subject increased notably since Ludovico il Moro had ordered an enormous bronze equestrian statue of his father, Francesco Sforza. The drawing in fig. 23 refers to this project which was never finished. The drawing on the opposite page (fig. 25) shows several men trying to lift a giant cannon: the drawing, probably made during one of his frequent visits to Milanese workshops some time around 1487, is important as proof of his growing and by then mature interest in firearms which were being produced in great quantities at that time as the arsenal in the shed in the background seems to suggest. Leonardo even studied the construction and the casting of cannons. Since one of the major obstacles to im-

proving the range and the precision of their fire lay in obtaining barrels with different lengths and smooth interiors, he devised a machine for profiling cannon pieces thus avoiding the difficulties of single casting techniques. The drawing in fig. 24 refers precisely to this extraordinary device: at the bottom a hydraulic turbine provides the power; the movement is then transmitted by a "never ending screw double crown wheel" mechanism to the screw which pushes the iron bar forward (on the right) which gets smoothed and cut in many homogeneous segments by the cutter which is set in motion by the complex mechanism on the left. Afterwards the various segments are connected and welded together thus obtaining more precise cannons of any size and shape.

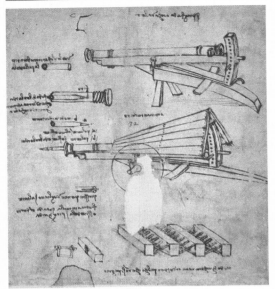

26

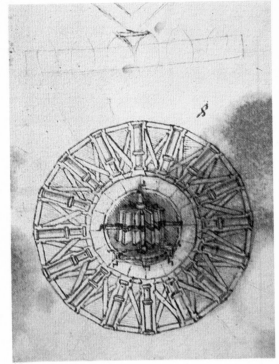

27

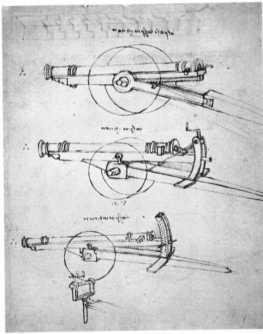

28

29

30

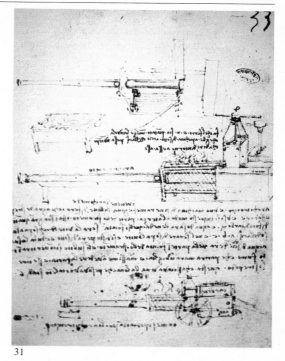

31

Leonardo prefers light weapons that can be carried by the infantry: a corollary of this dynamic conception of battle is the possibility of regulating the trajectory of the projectiles. In the drawings in figs. 26 and 28 the problem is solved by various types of elevating arcs. Another way to speed the operation is by using a movable rear breech which avoids the problems of loading through the mouth of the cannon.

Even naval battles interest Leonardo who, besides reviving the ancient Roman ramming ships equipped with devastatingly effective scythes, thought of equipping the boats with rapid and easy-to-use firearms like the "circumfolgore" (a rotating platform loaded with cannons; see fig. 27); or else with a large box-shaped mortar to be used by a single sailor. It was mounted on a rotating base and thus was capable of pouring a great deal of smoke and of fire bombs on to the unfortunate enemy ships (see fig. 29). He also checks out the alternatives to gunpowder: the most interesting one is the steam powered cannon which he claims to have copied from Archimedes and which he calls with a name which evokes the sound of thunder, "architronito" (fig. 31). it is a simply a copper cannon whose breech is heated by a brazier to a high temperature. Then water is poured into the red-hot breech and — as Leonardo says — «*immediately is converted to so much smoke that it will seem a miracle; specially at the sight of the fury and at the sound of the roar*». The pressure of the steam formed all of a sudden will be sufficient to shoot the iron ball lying in the barrel.

32

33

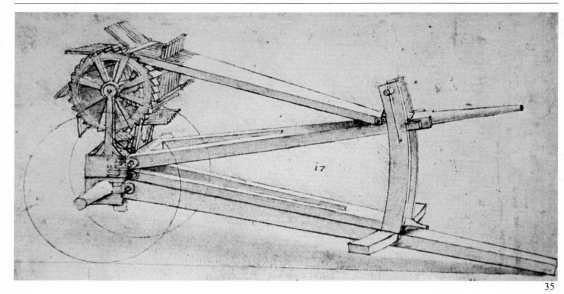

35

34. MACHINE GUNS Cod. Atl. f.56v.
35. MACHINE GUN Cod. Atl. f.3v.-a.

One of the problems that Leonardo poses in how to increase the volume and the speed of fire. He solves it by multiplying the number of barrels which he arranges in a fan shape as he has done in the machine at the center of the page in fig. 34, or else in a construction which he calls "an organ-pipe musket" (on the same sheet as the drawing cited above). It is a cart on which he has mounted three gun-racks each with eleven guns, for a total of 33 gunbursts. The device rotates so that while one rack is fired, the second one is reloaded and the third one cools off: thus it would be possible to increase the volume of fire and to insure its continuity. The weapons have a screw mechanism which regulates the elevating arc. The elegant drawing which appears in fig. 35 illustrates another example of a machine gun which several gun-racks and with an elevating arc.

36. EXPLOSIVE CANNON BALLS Cod. Atl. f.9v.-a.
37. ORIGINAL CANNON BALLS Cod. Arundel f.54r.
38. "COTOMBROT" Ms. B f.31v.

Leonardo realizes that while the iron cannon ball is useful against large and immobile targets like fortresses and bastions, that is of little use against small, moving targets like advancing troops. Against these targets he thinks of using explosive cannon balls which are shot by

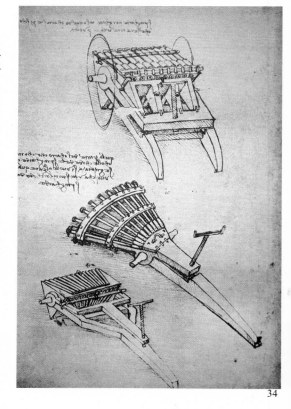

34

a large mortar and which shatter into many deadly fragments upon impact (fig. 36). He comments: «*It is the most deadly machine*

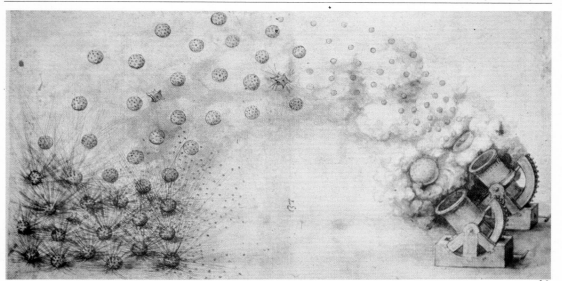

36

that exists. And when the cannon ball falls the nucleus sets fire to the other balls, and the central ball explodes and shatters the others which catch fire in the time it takes to say a "Hail Mary". And it has an outer shell which encloses everything». At times these explosive shells have a psychologial effect which is more than deadly. Leonardo enjoys describing the ones which appear in the drawing on the bottom of this page and have a strange name *"cotombrot"*: *«cannon ball a half foot wide full of small projectiles made of paper mixed with sulphur, pitch and "conocarsivo" which makes one sneeze when sniffed and in the middle there is gunpowder which lit sets fire to all of the projectiles and before it is thrown among the troops with a wick tied with a pouch and then the rockets scatter themselves over an area a hundred armlengths in diameter and whistle».*

The study of balistics is of major importance for the precision of fire. It allows Leonardo to understand, by means of experiments with streams of water, the influence of the air on the trajectory of cannon balls. He solves the problem drawing ogival projectiles (which are incredibly modern) which exploit an aerodynamic shape and directional wings (see fig. 37).

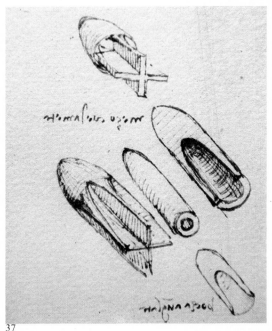

37

38

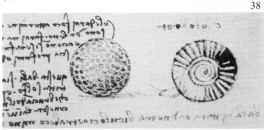

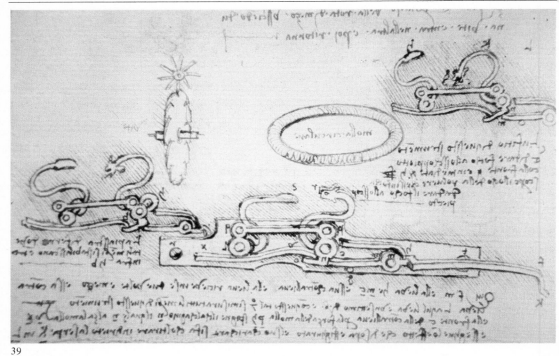

39

39. AUTOMATIC LIGHTER WITH A FUSE Cod. Madrid I, f.18v.

40. AUTOMATIC LIGHTER WITH A FLINT Cod. Atl. f.56v.-b.

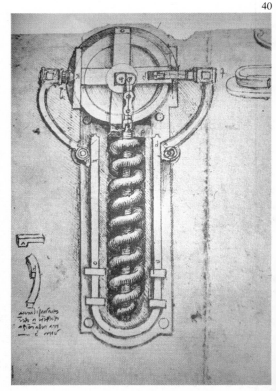

Leonardo didn't overlook the possibility of improving the lighting of firearms. The drawing in figure 39 shows, for example, three devices for opening the powder charge and setting fire to the charge at the same time. The fuse is lit in the "serpent's mouth" which is lowered then the trigger is pulled in order to set fire to the gunpowder whose container has been opened in the meantime.

Even more advanced is the design for an automatic lighter with a flint which, by the way, is an estremely beautiful technical drawing (fig. 40). On the right is the trigger, at the center a helicoidal spring which is linked by an adjustable chain to the wheel which as it turns rubs against the flint (on the left) and produces the spark.

HYDRAULIC MACHINES

Leonardo worked continuosly on water studies with great originality: there are many drawings and notes on the subject in the various codices and the idea of organizing his long familiarity with the material in a treatise must have occurred to him more than once even though it seems that the project ended soon after starting.

Although his interest in water studies probably started when he was young and he may have had some experience with fountains while working in Verrocchio's workshop in Florence, his sojourn in Lombardy certainly gave him the chance to apply his knowledge in a way that was impossible in Tuscany. In fact, advanced techniques of canalization had been in use in Lombardy for hydrographic reasons since ancient times. Leonardo, as the Duke's chief engineer, had to deal with this fundamental problem since both developing agriculture and providing power for machinery and for mills depended on its solution. The cultural tradition could offer him little help with this problem since, with the exception of Archimedes who was admired and studied by Leonardo, it had major difficulties dealing rationally with the fickleness and the instability of this liquid even though acqueducts, canals and other hydraulic projects had been carried out on a regular basis. Therefore Leonardo had to rely on personal experience and spent many days observing the flow of rivers and meditating on the incessant creation and destruction of forms in the water. These proposed fascinating analogies with the Universe to him as well as lofty thoughts about time, life and space which he was able to sum up in images with rare poetic qualities in the comments on his drawings and notes. From such careful observations he deduced many conclusions on motion, on erosion, on currents on the surface and at a certain depth. He often used wooden or glass models of canals where he created water currents which he dyed at times and dotted with small buoys at others in order to be able to follow the course of such an unstable element more easily. The results of such experiments were then applied to the practical problems of canalization as shown by the drawings of bulkheads, ports and locks with movable doors that remain in the codices.

41

Leonardo's thoughts even included a plan for directly operating on Nature by dredging a big navigable canal that would deviate from the course of the Arno connecting Florence with the sea through the area of Prato, Pistoia and Serravalle and guaranteeing the desired outlet in the Tyrrhenian Sea. Other ambitious hydraulic projects were planned for Lombardy, for Venetia where he planned to flood the Isonzo valley in the event of a Turkish invasion, and even for Latium where the Medici pope, Leo X, consulted him about reclaiming the Pontine swamps.

Fascinated by the thought of enabling man to move above and below the water Leonardo designed buoys and respirators, aided once again by a tradition which in order to satisfy military or practical needs had devoted much time to the problem throughout the Middle Ages and up into his own times. And he did not neglect to examine the possibility of speeding the motion of boats by perfecting the shape of their hulls to imitate the shape of fish, or else by using mechanisms which operated paddles from within the ship. Perhaps military purposes convinced him of the need for a boat with a double hull capable of resisting damage of the kind he planned to inflict on the enemy by means of screw devices for crushing and for secretly anchoring the hulls of the boats to the sea floor. Such a task would have been entrusted to men equipped with diving suits or else transported underwater in a fascinating but undefined submarine.

Leonardo had already mentioned his ability « *to conduct water from one place to another* » in the famous letter written to Lodovico il Moro. However even in this case, it was experience that broadened his horizons to include hydrodynamics, a science which is closely linked to the exploitation of this form of energy. There are extraordinary drawings of whirlpools and of eddies where one senses the strength of the water and there are also drawings of wheels for harnessing water power which are just as extraordinary.

The need to provide urban centers with water, to drain basins or swamps together with other hydraulic endeavors involved Leonardo in the task of perfecting pumps and other machines known since antiquity: "Archimedes' screws" and water wheels fill the pages of the codices by Francesco di Giorgio Martini and other engineers of his generation, but in Leonardo's works they reach a graphic and functional perfect unknown elsewhere.

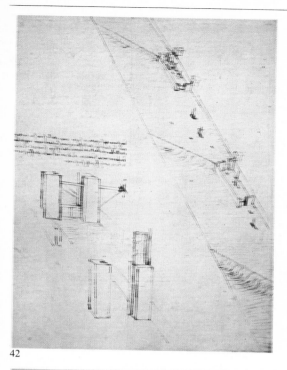

42

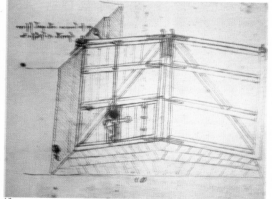

43

41. WHIRLPOOL B.R. WINDSOR 12660v.
42. CANAL WITH LOCKS Cod. Atl. f.33v.

The drawing (fig. 42) dates from the period of experiments in Lombardy. We see a river or a canal which flows over a gradient that can be a overcome by a boats thanks to a series of locks. The boats enter a basin whose water level can be controlled by opening or closing the gates which let the water come in or go out so that the boats can reach the height necessary to overcome the obstacle. There are even drawings of the doors that can be slid sideways and which are particularly useful because they do not limit the height of the ships.

43. GATE FOR A LOCK Cod. Atl. f.240r.-c.

Leonardo perfected the systems for opening and closing the gates as this drawing shows. He designed a small sluice-gate with a bolt at the bottom of the gate. It would have let in enough water to balance the pressure on the two sides of the main gate thus making it easier to open it.

44. DREDGE Ms. E f. 75v.
45. MODEL OF A DREDGE Museum of Milan

For the maintenance and cleaning of canals or of lacustrine basins Leonardo invented a dredge mounted between two boats and equipped with four blades (set in rotation by moving a crank) deliberately designed to remove the slime from the bottom and to deposit it on a raft moored between the two boats. As the wheel turns a rope tied to the bank winds itself around the drum shaped axle and automatically changes the work area. It's also possible to raise the axle vertically in order to regulate the depth of the excavation.

44

45

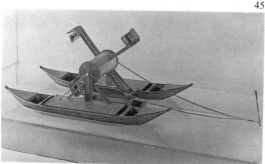

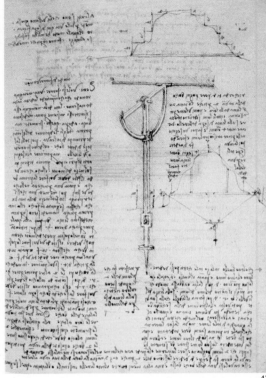

46

47

46. CANAL FROM FROM FLORENCE TO THE SEA
   Cod. Madrid II, f.22v. e 23r.

The idea of an artificial canal between Florence and the sea was not news to the minds of the Florentines. Leonardo became interested in the project on several occasions. According to his plans the canal would have changed the course of the Arno river towards Prato, Pistoia and Serravalle and would have rejoned its natural course before reaching Pisa. Thus it woulds have become possible to irrigate the region abundantly and to navigate the route between Florence and Pisa which Nature had made winding and difficult.
The possibility of actually carrying out the project arose during the war against Pisa at the beginning of the 1500's. In fact, many Florentines, including Machiavelli backed the venture hoping to cut the enemy city out of the course of the Arno. The work was actually began and its seems under the direction of Leonardo who had just returned from northern Italy, but it was soon abandoned for technical reasons and because of the obstacles posed by the Pisans.

47. THE SERRAVALLE TUNNEL Cod. Madrid II, f. 111r.

Leonardo had planned on having the canal pass under the saddle of Serravalle, near Pistoia. The drawing shows his daring excavation plans.

48. EXCAVATING MACHINE Cod. Atl. f.1v.-b.
49. EXCAVATING MACHINE Cod. Atl. f.1.v-a.

Rather than actually meant for digging, Leonardo's excavating machines were intended for lifting and moving the excavated material thus notably aiding the workers' efforts. They are probably connected with the project for canalizing the Arno river which called for the excavation of a ditch 18 meters wide and 6 meters deep. In fact, the drawings seem to indicate the right size for the machine and for

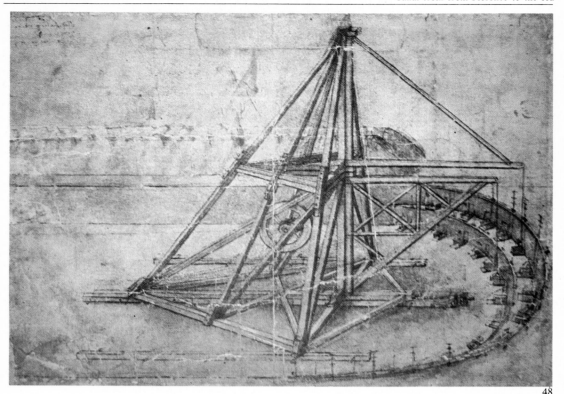

48

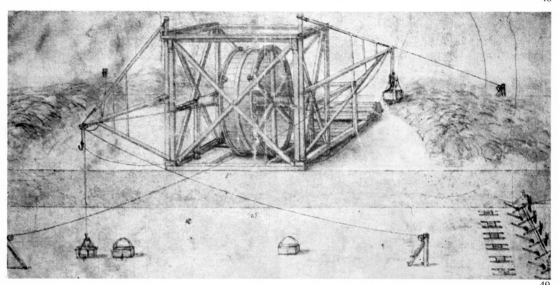

49

the canal which is being dug. The crane with rearms of various lengths is especially interesting (fig. 48) since it can be used with a series of counter weights on two or more levels of excavation. The arms can also be rotated 180° so that they can cover the whole width of the canal. The machine is mounted on tracks and can be moved forward as the work progresses by means of a screw mechanism on the central rail.

50

51

52

50. SYSTEM FOR WALKING ON THE WATER Cod. Atl. f.7.r.

51. 52. WAYS TO BREATHE UNDER WATER Cod. Atl. 7r.-a.

53. LIFEBUOY Cod. Atl. f.276v.

54. BREATHING TUBE Cod. Arundel f.24v.

55. WEBBED GLOVES Ms. B f.81v.

56. DIVING SUIT Cod. Atl. f.333v.

The lifebuoy, the webbed gloves and even the system for walking on the water using floating shoes and poles cannot be considered innovations. They are all inventions which are as old as history itself. If one really insists on finding precedents then one only needs to thumb through a few medieval codices which in turn derive from Archimedes and other antique sources. All the same these drawings by Leonardo are strange, rapid and extremely enjoyable while seeming to reveal Man's pleasure in winning the battle against the elements. Leonardo is certainly not the first person interested in enabling Man to submerge in and remain under water. Once again medieval codices throughly illustrate the problem, while contemporary experiments like those done by Leon Battista Alberti in connection with the possibility of recovering some Roman ships on the bottom of Lake Nemi. However Leonardo, as on other occasions, shows such an ability in the drawings and such an attention for details that he foreshadows modern solutions. His diving suit, for example, was supposed to be made from perfectly water-proofed leather and with a large breast pocket that could be filled with air in order to increase its volume, thus facilitating the ascent (fig. 56). Leonardo's diver was also equipped with a flexible breathing tube (see fig. 54) which connects the hood with a protective floating dome on the surface (preferably made of reeds and leather joints). Next to the whole apparatus Leonardo has also drawn the details of the valves for the intake and the outlet of the air.

53

55

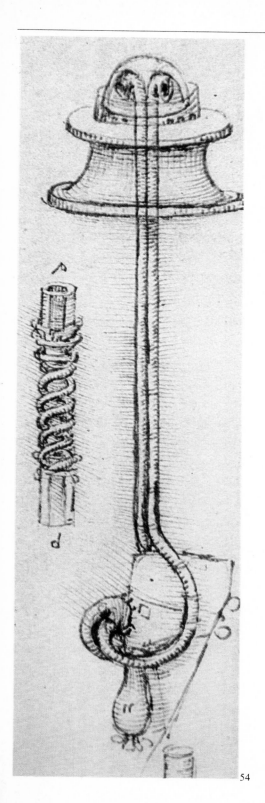

54

56

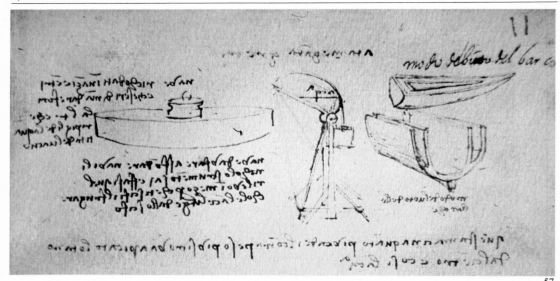

57

57. BOAT WITH A DOUBLE HULL AND SUBMARINE Ms. B.f.11.r
58. SHIP WRECKE Cod. Atl. f.333v.

Among the inventions which are attributed to Leonardo the "submarine" in particularly fascinating because it foreshadows the distant future. The hypothesis that Leonardo actually thought of building a ship capable of submerging and returning to the surface seems plausible considering the drawing on the left side on the page shown in fig. 57 and interpreting some of his sentences. For example on pages that deal with boats and ships Leonardo writes: « *When you want to remain above blow up a goatskin and pull the weight below and walk* »; commenting on the drawing shown here he suggests to the sailor that before « *entering and shutting yourself in, put on the I and you compensate for the amount of vacuum* ». It is impossible to deny that Leonardo possessed the necessary knowledge of hydrostatics. In addition he could have been inspired by the submarine that Cesariano had built and tested in the moat around the castle in Milan. Leonardo's vessel probably submerged using a system of weights and ballasts; and resurfaced by forcing air into compartments built for this purpose in the hull. Propulsion could have been provided by sails while it was on the surface and by oars or fins while it was underwater.

The double-hulled boat which appears on the same page has often been connected with the

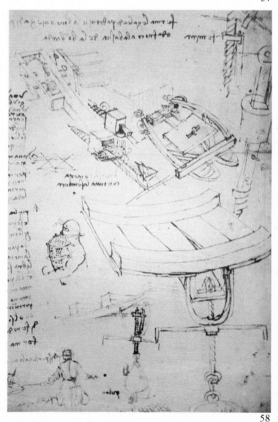

58

studies on submersion. Yet it seems more feasible that it was a system for defence during maritime warfare, especially useful against the

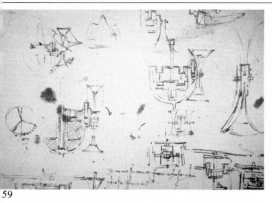

59

60

61

62

hull-crushing device in figure 58. It seems to be a kind of tuning fork that a diver was supposed to secretly stick into the planking of an enemy ship; it is a screw device capable of crushing wooden boards. Another technique that Leonardo proposes for underwater warfare involves tying the hull of the ship to the bottom of the sea with a screw mechanism. When the ship set sail its disemboweling and sinking would have been guaranteed.

59. PADDLE BOAT Cod. Atl. f.384r.
60. MODEL OF A PADDLE BOAT Museum of Vinci
61. PADDLE VESSEL Ms. B f.83.r.
62. FISH SHAPES Ms. G f.50v.

One of the problems that Leonardo tackles is how to speed and to ease navigation. Naturally the shape of the hull had a primary importance and Leonardo used the shapes of fish as models since they are at home in the water. He also thought of equipping some boats with large paddles which would have been worked by hand or foot cranks perhaps aided by flywheels, thus increasing the rhythm and efficiency of traditional oars. In the dynamic drawing reproduced in figure number 61 one has a sense of the vessel's agility (it has a tapered prow and operates on the surface of the water) as well as its manoeuverability which is made possible by the fact that the rower faces forward.

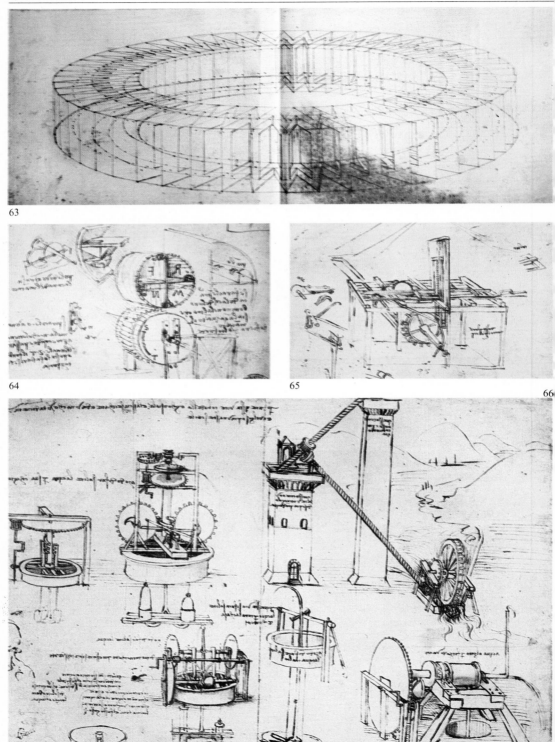

63

64

65

66

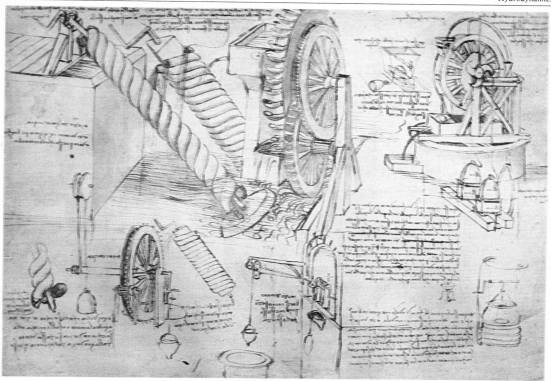

67

63. WATER WHEEL Cod. Atl. f.263r.-a.

Harnessing water power is fundamental for running machinery and mills. Leonardo applied himself quite often to the study of hydrodynamics and even thought out the most efficient way of exploiting water power using big wheels like the one shown here in an extraordinary geometric drawing.

64. VENTILATOR Ms. B f.82r.

Another application of hydrodynamics in the one suggested by Leonardo for a device that could compress air and force it through ducts. Its purpose could have been one of many ranging from ventilating rooms to feeding furnaces. According to the drawing it was a kind of cylindrical drum externally covered with wings for propulsion (by water or by hand) and internally divided in four interconnected sections with valve openings between them that let the compressed air out. A certain amount of water circulates inside it, passing from one section to another as the drum rotates, com-

pressing the air and forcing in out of the tube in the middle.

65. HYDRAULIC SAW Cod. Atl. f.389r.

There are many machines which can use water power. For example, we show a hydraulic saw here. The current sets in motion the wheel which in turn activates both the vertical saw and the bogie where the trunk lies. Thus the operation becomes automatic.

66. WAY TO LIFT WATER IN TWO PHASES Cod. Atl. f.386r.
67. ARCHIMEDES' SCREWS AND WATER WHEELS Cod. Atl. f.386.r.
68. TUBES AND A DRILL Cod. Madrid I, f.25v.
69. WATER WHEEL WITH CUPS Cod. Atl. 386v.b.

These machines for lifting water certainly cannot be considered innovations since it seems that they were known as far back as ancient Egyptian times and were later studied in the Greek world, especially by Archimedes.

In the Renaissance all engineers were acquainted with them and put them to use on a regular basis. Leonardo drew a great and varied number of them, often adding ingeniuos improvements and always using his extraordinary esthetic sense.

For example we can cite the so-called "Archimedes' screw" (fig. 67) which is a tube tightly coiled around an appropriately inclined cylinder that draws water from a basin up to the upper end of the spiral out of which the liquid gushed continuously driven from the bottom to the top by the rotation of a crank. The same system can be doubled (as is the case in fig. 66) in order to fill tower shaped water reservoirs. In this case the rotation of the spirals depends on the power provided by a water wheel and by gears at the mid-point which transmit the motion to other "screws". The reservoir might have been meant to supply water to a city through wooden tubes. Leonardo had done research on their joints and on techniques for boring them with a drill (see figure 68).

Another technique for pumping water is to force air through bellows creating big bubbles which drive the liquid upwards. Then one can also use a water wheel with cups that takes water from a lower-basin, which is always kept full to the brim, and empties it into the upper basin (figs. 67 and 69).

The uses for such machinery are varied and commonplace: they range from fountains to supplying water, from water games to the draining of swamps.

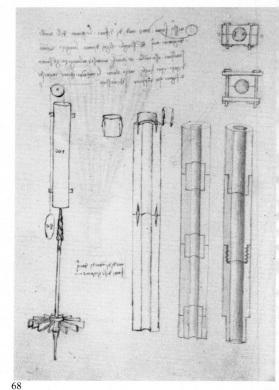

68

69

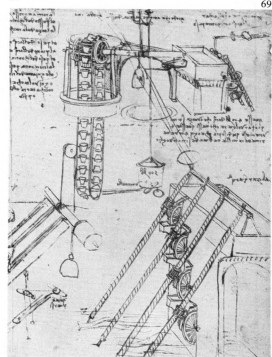

MACHINES FOR FLIGHT

Man's desire to dominate the lightest and most impalpable of the elements, air, goes back as far as the legend of Icarus and follows a slender thread of hope until it research the Reinaissance's renewed faith and until Leonardo's great mind takes it up again. He is convinced that «Man forcing his big artificial wings against the resistant air, winning, [can] rule and rise above it».

Armed with the enthusiasm of such a convinction Leonardo began to work on a machine powered by muscular activity alone that would allow a man to hover in the air by moving its wings like birds do. There are many drawings which show the various kinds of "ornitotteri", the flying machines designed by Leonardo. There are also some which show a man prone and intent on operating the mechanisms connected to the wings; others show propulsion by more complete screw and pulley systems; while others show a man in a vertical position in a flying vessel pushing the pedals of the device with his arms and legs.

The design of the ornitottero's wings clearly had to derive from nature: Leonardo studies the anatomy of birds' wings and analyzes the function and the distribution of their feathers. He observes their flight and notes that a bird's wings beat differently when it wants to remain in the same place, to move forward and to land. He also stops to consider the bat's jointed and membranous wing carefully. On the basis of these and another observations he designs large wings meant to enable man not only to take off but also direct his flight once he is in mid-air thanks to ailerons and joints. He studies these so as to be able to imitate birds' airy acrobatics and their economy of energy in flight with ever increasing precision. Until the end of the century Leonardo believed that he would have been able to carry out his ambitious project for mechanical flight. Yet the limits on muscle power, the real root of the problem, must have worried him quite a bit, since at that time we find him intent on substituting it with a crossbow mechanism which might have guaranteed its propulsion but certainly would not have solved the problem of autonomy in flight created by the spring's rapid unwinding.

At the beginning of the fifteen hundreds Leonardo is back in Tuscany where he conducted extremely profitable research on birds' flight for the three years between 1503 and 1506. His systematic investigation of its relationship with the atmospheric condition, with the presence or absence of wind, with related meterological and aerodynamic phenomena brought Leonardo's fervid mind to abandon the old idea of an "instrument" based on wing movement and to take up that of «*flight without wing movement*».

Observing that large birds of prey let themselves be carried by the air currents, — perhaps inspired by the nobility of these animals and by the altitudes they fly at —, he thought of equipping a man with large jointed wings which would enable him to reach the favourable currents using simple body movements and wasting little energy, so that he could be carried by them until descrending like a «*dead leaf*».

A new burst on enthusiasm must have accompanied this idea as the famous prophecy seems to reflect: «*the great bird will take to the air for the first time, off the back of its magnificient Cècero filling the universe with wonder, filling all the writings with his fame and the nest where he was born with eternal glory*». As far as the legend of Zoroastro is concerned, the one about the unlucky mechanic-inventor who tried to fly the machine off the top of mount Cèceri near Fiesole which has often been connected with Leonardo's words, we must trace its origin in someone's imagination until we find proof to the contrary.

If it's true that Nature provided the departure point for his flight experiments, then it's also true that over the years of experiences Leonardo devoted more and more time to them so that he became — according to the well chosen words written by a famous Da Vinci scholar — an «*aeronaut, aerodynamicist, aerotechnician and observer of birds' flight*». We mean that the systematic research that he had undertaken at the beginning of the century had brought him to study «*the quality and the thickness of the air*» — and he designs hydroscopic instruments for this purpose —, the wind's velocity and its variation — and now it's the anemometer's turn —, and the "reaction" of air which enables birds as heavy as eagles and vultures to move upwards when it is moved in great quantities. The last one is based on a principle quite similar to the laws of hydrostatics, a fact which stresses Leonardo's belief that water science was the mirror image of wind science

70

« which [wind science] we will show » — writes Leonardo — *« through water's motion through itself and this sensible science will become a step towards understanding birds' flight through air and wind »*.

Thus the wind, like the currents in a river, forms eddies and whirlpools and has its own laws of dynamics and statics. Understanding them will enable Man to truly rule the air. The parachute, the helicopter and even more so the glider are the products of such an intimate understanding of Nature and necessarily open the doors on Man's future.

70. EAGLE AND BAT Ms. B f.89v.

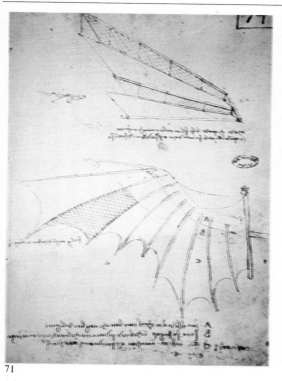

71

72

73

71. STUDY OF A WING WITH OPENINGS Cod. Atl. f.74r.

72. STUDY OF A WING WITH OPENING Cod. Atl. f.309v.-b.

This is probably the first type of wing studied by Leonardo. Observing the downwards distribution of bird's feathers (overlapping and close in order to offer a rigid surface to the air) he deduces, erroneously however, that when they take off they spread the feathers to allow air to pass through them. Intending to imitate nature's majesty he designs them with movable doors that open for take off and close in order to offer the compact wing surface needed to press against the air. In the upper part of the two sheets the "doors" are drawn and the materials to be used — net, cane, paper — are indicated. Perhaps Leonardo actually thought of constructing this kind of wing and in the drawing shown in figure 71 he notes:

A *will be young fir, which has fibre and is light*

B *will be fustian with feathers glued to it so that the air won't escape*

C *be starched taffeta and for the trial you will use thin paper*

73. MODEL OF AN ARTICULATED WING (see fig. 78) Museum of Vinci

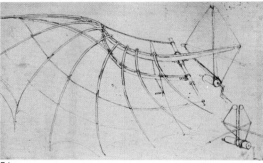

74

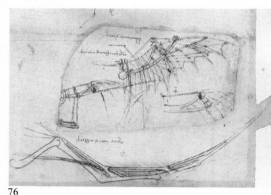

75

76

74. STUDY OF A WING IN ONE PIECE Cod. Atl. f.313r.-a

After the trial wings with doors, Leonardo directs his interest towards a "united" wing which, like that of a bat, was supposed to have a single "cloth" stretched over a structure in wood and cane. The crank mechanism that sets the wings in motion and that also winds the rope around a reel is quite interesting. The pilot was supposed to sit in the nacelle.

75. WING STUDY Cod. Atl. f.22v.-b

Probably dating from the first years of the fifteen hundreds, the drawing in fig. 75 shows the project for a wing which is more sophisticated both for the materials used and for its imitation of birds' joints. It seems quite similar to the studies of sail flight.

76. WING STUDY Cod. Atl. f.311v.-d

Another drawing of a "united" wing but this time it is divided in two sections. The external one can be rotated.

77. STUDY FOR A WING WITH JOINTS Cod. Atl. f.341r.

There are many studies of wing joints and the drawing that we show on the opposite page, datable after 1490, is one of the most sophisticated elaborations. Leonardo illustrates the movements of the wing and accompanies the image with an explanatory text. At points C and D there are two handles which move the wings by alternately winding the ropes around reels. The handles (C and D) are pushed by one hand and one heel which Leonardo insists must be moved in sincrony. Once set in motion the lever AE is raised while, thanks to the joint at E, the rest of the instrument (from E to L) is lowered. The system of cords and joints (VTP and OSG) serve to rotate the wing so that it cuts the air when it is moved forward and it pushes the air when moved backward. The rotation system is worked with the tip of the foot which moves the lever AB, in turn connected with a system of cords. The wing was intended for an "ornitottero" of the vertical type.

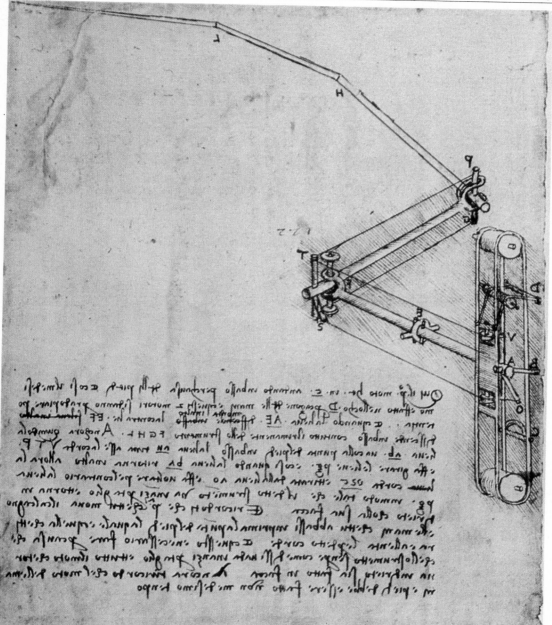

77

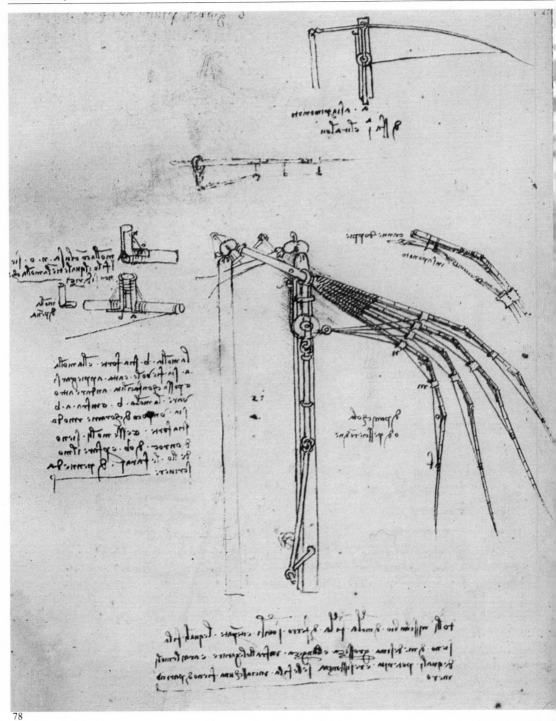

78

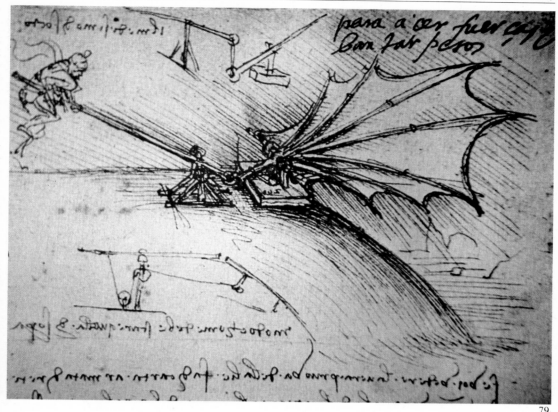

79

78. STUDY OF A JOINTED WING Cod. Atl. f.308r.-a.

This drawing of an uncertain date shows a complicated series of spring joints for the automatic return of the bent wing. The joints are all connected by tie-rods. Details of the springs (made from horn or from metal) are drawn on the upper left part of the page. The perfection of these complex traction and torsion mechanisms reflects the need to faithfully copy the wing motion of birds while easing the task for the man operating it.

**79. TEST FOR THE WING OF AN "ORNITOTTERO"
Ms. B f.88v.**

Leonardo comments this self-explanatory drawing: «*If you want to see a real test for the wings, make a wing from paper with a net and cane structure 20 armlenghts long and wide [around 12 meters], and attach it on a plank which weighs 200 pounds; and apply, as shown above, a sudden force. And if the 200 pound plank lifts itself before the wing descends then the trial can be considered successful; but be sure that the force is rapid and if the above effect is not obtained, waste no more time on it*».

**80. MODEL OF A FLYING MACHINE
Museum of Milan**

80

51

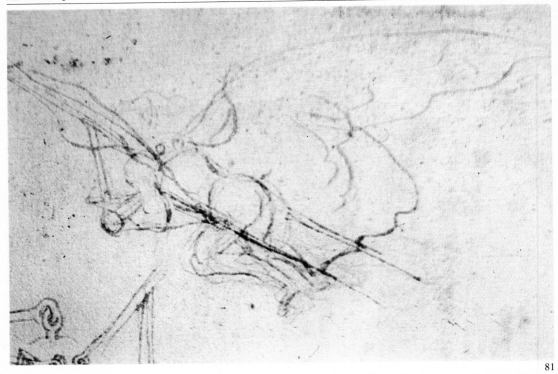

81

81. THE FLYING MACHINE Cod. Atl. f.276r.-b.

This is one of Leonardo's first studies on the subject. The wing movement depends on the alternating motion of the hands and the feet. These, in stirrups, push a system of levers that lower the wing which is then raised by other levers operated by hand. The drawing, rapid and abbreviated, captures the ecitement of his first contact with Man's great dream of ruling the air.

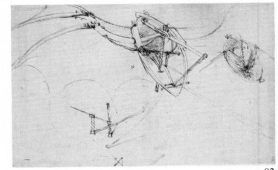

82

82. "ORNITOTTERO" WITH A NACELLE Cod. Atl. f.313v.-a.

This drawing, which has a fuselage shaped like a boat for the pilot, proves that Leonardo often thought of air in the same terms as water. The large bat-like wings are operated by a system of screws and nuts (see also the detail study at the bottom). As in boats a rudder has been provided. The wide tail plane, perhaps intended for controlling the altitude, is quite interesting.

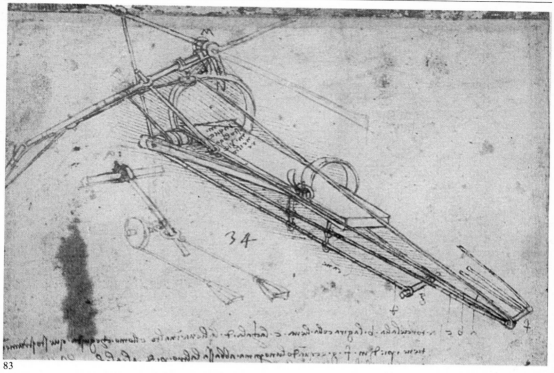

83

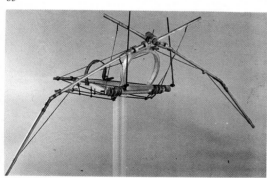

84

83. PRONE "ORNITOTTERO" Cod. Atl. f. 302v.-a.

The drawing in fig. 83, one of the most famous ones on flight, is very precise and is accompanied by useful explanations: «*A rotates the wing, B turns it with a lever, C lowers it, D raises it*»; the man lies stretched out on the platform (the writing reads: «*on this site the heart is placed*») and puts his feet in the stirrups F and G one of which raises the wing while the other lowers it. Thus we have a flying machine in which a man, lying prone, pushes pedals that operate the raising and the lowering of the wing as well as its bending and rotation by means of cords and levers as it practically "rows" through the air.

84. MODEL OF AN "ORNITOTTERO"
(see fig. 83), Museum of Milan

85. PRONE "ORNITOTTERO" WITH A RUDDER
Ms. B f.75r.

Although essentially like the preceding "orni-tottero", the one in figure 85, still has a few interesting variations: the pilot enters the metal half circle and bears the apparatus on his back; the movement of the wings still rely's on the movement of the feet, in this case helped by the hands that operate the handles under the half circle. The most interesting difference is « *the rudder mounted on the neck* » which is the object with fins on the machine's tail that appears in the detail study on the upper right side. The direction is controlled by head movements.

86. PRONE "ORNITOTTERO" WITH FOUR WINGS
Ms. B f.79r.

In this case we have a flying machine with four wings operated by the pilot's hands and feet. The former raise the wings using a reel once the feet have lowered one pair of wings at a time. Thus the rhythm in the wing movement has been increased to a speed that the rapidity of the sketch seems to reflect. The apparatus mounted on the pilot's shoulders is interesting. It depends on the winding and unwinding of ropes around reels.

87. MODEL OF A FLYING MACHINE
Museum of Vinci

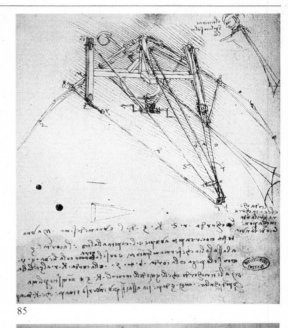

85

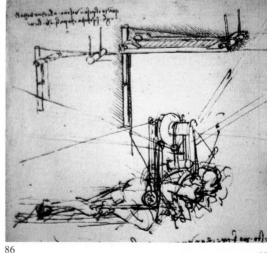

86

87

88. VERTICAL "ORNITOTTERO"

The need for a greater energy source forces
Leonardo to use all the parts of the human body in an almost obsessed research: in the drawing we see a man intent on operating the well
known sliding mechanisms not only with his
hands and feet, but even with his head, which
— according to Leonardo — *« will have a
strength equal to 200 pounds »*. The man
stands erect in the middle of an enormous vessel. Leonardo gives us its dimensions: the nacelle is 12 meters long; the ladder 12 from the
ground; the wing span 24 meters with a movement of 4,8. Given the size of the apparatus
Leonardo thought that two pairs of wings
would have been needed, beating « criss-cross,
the way a horse moves ».

89. A TAKEOFF AND LANDING SYSTEM FOR THE VERTICLE "ORNITOTTERO" Ms. B f.89r.

The drawing is self-explanatory and shows
three different sequences of the use of the re-
tractible ladders that Leonardo planned to put
on vertical "ornitottero". Once again Nature
has provided the inspiration as Leonardo actually admits: *« see the swift which put on the
ground cannot take-off because it has short
legs; and when it is off the ground pull the ladders up as shown in the second figure above »*;
and he adds, *« this is how you should take-off
from a plain. These ladders serve as legs and it
can beat its wings as they are born »*. Then as
far as landing is concerned he writes: *« These
hooks [they are concave wedges; see the detail
on the right] which are attached to the foot of
the ladder and serve the same purpose as the
tips of the toes of a person who jumps on them
so that his whole body doesn't shake like it
would if he jumped on his heels »*.

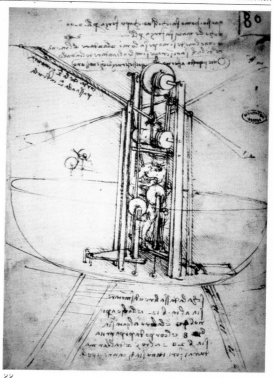

88

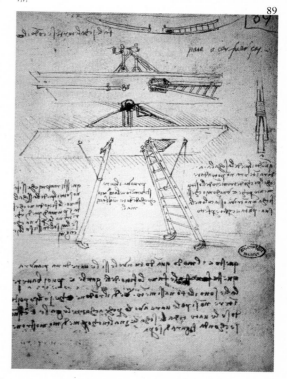

89

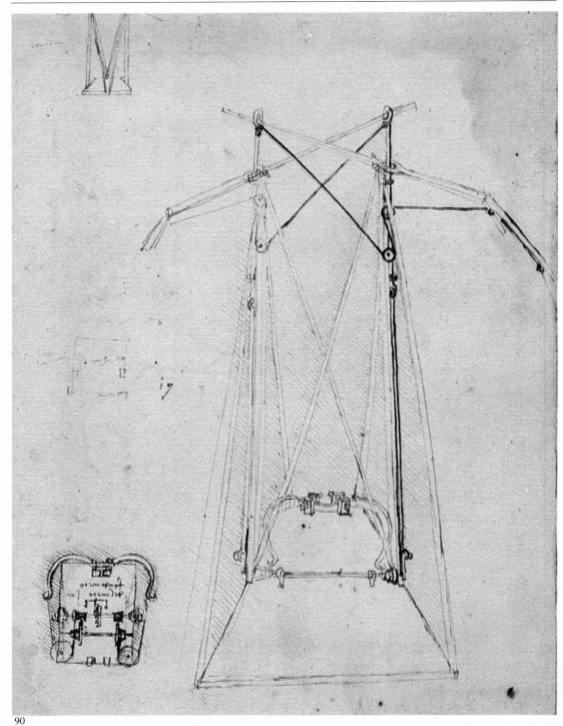

90

91

92

90. CROSS-BOW "ORNITOTTERO" Cod. Atl. f.314r.-b

Perhaps because he was convinced that is was impossible to operate such a machine using mere muscle power, Leonardo thought out alternative solutions like the one with a spring device which would transmit its energy to the wings of the "ornitottero" (in this case a vertical one) as it unwound. In the detail study on the left Leonardo has drawn a device similar to ones he uses in his "automobile" and in certain clock mechanisms. The system, which in theory is so far ahead of its times that it has even been called "Leonardo's airplane", in practice is unsatisfactory because of the necessarily rapid unwinding of the spring and because of the difficulty of rewinding it while flying.

91. BIRDS' FLIGHT Cod. Volo Uccelli f.8r.
92. BIRDS' FLIGHT Cod. Volo Uccelli f.7v.

His systematic study on flight in nature explains the about-face in Leonardo's mind where glide-flying substitutes fight by wing motion. Around 1505 the «*Codice sul Volo degli Uccelli*» (now in Turin, in the ex-Royal Library) had been finished. The drawings we show come from this work.

93. "ORNITOTTERO" WITH A SEMI-RIGID WING Cod. Atl. f.309v.-a.

This isn't really a glider which is guided by the pilot's movements, but it is an interesting hybrid in any case. The pilot hangs vertically at the center of the machine and the wing tips have joints to be used to control the apparatus while the rigid structure is made for supporting it.

94

95

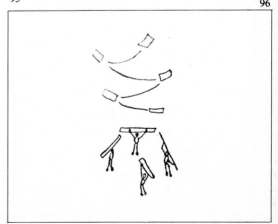

96

93

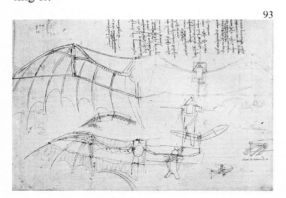

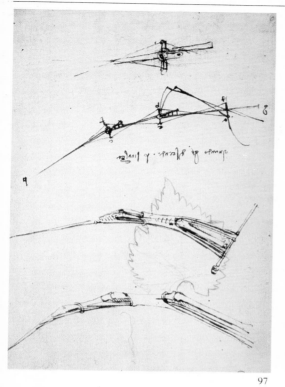

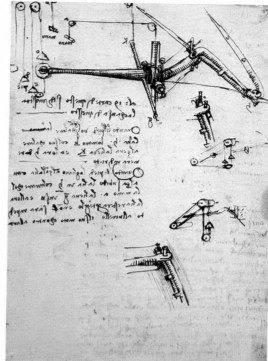

97

98

94. EQUILIBRIUM STUDY
   Cod. Volo Uccelli f.16v.

95. BALANCE STUDY Cod. Volo Uccelli f.5r.

96. "DEAD-LEAF" DESCENT Ms. G. f.74r.

97. WING STUDY FOR A GLIDER
   Cod. Volo Uccelli f.17r.

No drawings exists of Leonardo's glider whose shape and operation have been deduced from excerpts and sketches from several codices and primarily from the one on birds' flight. We know that it was to be built with light materials: bamboo and cloth, with bindings and stay-rods in raw silk or in special leather and with joints in the same leather. A tall cane structure with a cylindrical or parallelepiped shape was probably slung from its very wide wings (about 10 meters wide). The pilot was placed far below the wings in this structure in order to insure stability. On this subject there is also a study on glider equilibrium (shown here in fig. 94) which was made with the intent of determining — as Leonardo says — «*the bird's center of gravity, without which, such an "instrument" would have little worth*».
In order to take-off the pilot was supposed to turn the wings so that he would be lifted by favorable currents. In fact the wings could be raised and lowered using a system of ropes and pulleys worked with his feet (in stirrups) and his hands (operating handles). While being raised and lowered, the wings were also bent and stretched out again using an automatic system of rods, levers and joints (on this subject see the drawings reproduced in figs. 97-98). The movements of the glider in flight thus were controlled by movable wings which sought out the wind and by the pilot's balancing. Leonardo did a sketch (fig. 95) on this subject where he comments: «*[the man must] be free from the waist down so that he can balance himself, as though he were in a boat, and so that his center of gravity and that of the structure can be balanced and adjusted*».
Last of all there are the studies on descent shown here in fig. 96 with the comment: «*the man will move to the right if he bends his right arm and extends his left one; and he will move from right to left by changing the arms' positions*».

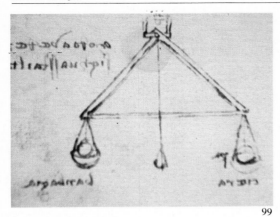

99

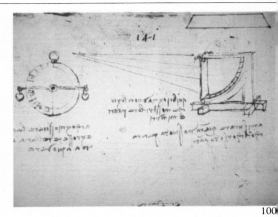

100

99. HYGROSCOPE Cod. Atl. 8v-b.

100. HYGROSCOPE AND ANEMOMETER Cod. Atl. f. 249v.-a.

Alberti had already invented this instrument (fig. 99) which is a simple set of scales with a hygroscopic substance on one side (cotton wool, sponge etc.) and wax, which does not absorb water, on the other one. It is used as Leonardo says, to "know the quality and the thickness of air and when it's going to rain". Naturally the reading is taken by noting how much the side with the hygroscopic material has descended.

101. ANEMOMETERS Cod. Arundel f.24r.

Leonardo designed two different kinds of instru-

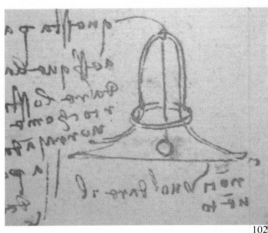

102

101

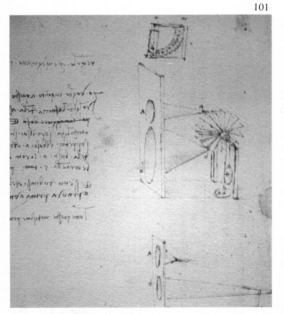

ments for measuring the wind's velocity. The first one (on the upper part of fig. 101 and on the right side of fig. 100) is called a "lamellae anemometer" or "brush" (since traditionally feathers were used to test the wind): it is simply a graduated stick with a lamella which moves more or less according to the wind's intensity. The other one which appears on the same page of the Arundel Codex is made from cone shaped tubes and can be used to check whether the wind which turns the wheel is proportionate to the opening in the cones that admit the air, since the intensity of the wind is identical.

102. SLOPE METER Cod. Atl. f.38r.-a.

It is simply a pendulum inside a glass bell jar (to avoid drafts) which — according to Leonardo — helps to «*steer the instrument [the flying machine] straight or crooked, as you prefer, that is, when you want to fly straight*

103

104

make the ball stay in the middle of the circle...».

103. AIR "SCREW" Ms. B f.38v.

This is one of Leonardo's most famous drawings which many consider the ancestor of the modern helicopter. It is a screw with a radius of 4,8 meters, a metal border and a linen cover which is set in rotation by men pushing levers as they walk around the shaft or else by rapidly unwinding the rope under the axle. On this subject Leonardo wrote: «*I think, if this screw instrument is well made, that means made from linen starched (to block its pores) and is turned rapidly, then said screw will find its female in the air and will climb upwards*».

104. PARACHUTE Cod. Atl. f.381v.-a.

«*If a man has a tent made of clogged cloth each side of which is 12 armlengths wide and which is 12 tall, then he can jump from any great altitude without hurting himself*». These words and the image itself are so eloquent that there is no need for further explanations.

LEONARDO'S MECHANICS

The Crusca dictionary says that mechanics: « *is the science which deals with the equilibrium and the motion of both solid and liquid bodies; and is also the Art which teaches us how to build all sorts of machines, instruments, devices and similar things* ».

Leonardo dedicated himself to this "Art" with such constancy that he filled three quarters of the surviving codices with inventions and studies that he may have planned to organize in a major treatise on mechanics. However his notes only speak of four volumes, now considered lost, in which he dealt with « *mechanical elements* ». The discovery of the Madrid Codices widened our knowledge of Leonardo's work on mechanical elements considerably since Madrid I has been hypothetically identified as one of the four volumes he mentions.

Leonardo's undeniable theoretical contribution to science in his studies on « *weight, force, thrust and impact... movement's children...* » springs both from his need for clarity, from his deductive logic and from experience in his favorite mechanical art, which are all documented in the codices that contain drawings of machines' constituent parts and of the devices for the transmission of motion.

There are five simple machines that have been used since ancient times: the winch, the lever, the pulley, the wedge and the screw. Leonardo not only shows us that he knows them well but also increased their use and their specificity so that he could use them in complex mechanisms which automatically activate other operations. Explicitly or implicitly all these simple machines appear in all of Leonardo's inventions, but it's worth concentrating on the attention that he reserves for the "screw". This machine, associated with other parts, can be put to use in many ways and for this reason appears in most of his machinery.

On a page in the Madrid Codex Leonardo speaks at length about the « *nature of the screw and of its use, and how it should be used to pull rather than to push; and how it is stronger if it is single rather than double, and thin rather than thick... and how many kinds of never-ending screws can be made and how the never-ending screw can be paired with cog wheels...* ». In short a complete list of the varieties and of the possibilities offered by the screw which Leonardo interprets as a symbol of Nature's great strength.

The moving part which appears most frequently in Leonardo's machines is the cog wheel. We have broad graphic documentation on the subject, including the problem of the profile of the cogs to be used.

A pair that he often uses for transmitting motion is the "peg wheel-cage rochet" mechanism, which he occasionally substitutes, when dealing with oblique axles and when lifting great weights, with another pair of mechanisms, the cogwheel and the "endless screw" which guarantee the irreversibility of the motion and have the mechanical advantage of being very strong when made from resistant materials.

In order to obtain major changes in velocity Leonardo uses "reduction gears" instead of the pulley and belt system; and it's a wonder that he drew perfect designs for flexible chains without ever thinking of using them to transmit either continuous motion between two gears, discontinuous motion — as in the case of clock mechanisms — by attaching them to a weight, or spring energy as in the case of the automatic lighter.

Directly linked to the problem of transmitting motion is the research on friction which lead to the use of bearings, a solution which is still valid today. Simple lubrification is not sufficient to solve the problem of part wear which Leonardo tries at first to avoid by arranging the axles in a way which reduces the friction as much as possible; later he tries bearings made from anti-friction metal (an alloy of copper and tin) and finally comes up with various types of ball bearings which are the forerunners of those we use today.

Leonardo's machines not only transmit motion but also transform it: from continuous to alternating as happens in the machines for polishing lenses based on the already well known connecting rod-crank mehanism (at times aided by a fly-wheel) or, vice versa, from alternating to continuous as in the case of certain weight-lifting machines. We must remember that the energy sources available to Leonardo for operating his machinery were the traditional ones: human and animal muscle power; wind; water; crossbow and spring systems; weights and counterweights; and occasionally steam. And the materials, the techniques and the mechanics that his era could offer, certainly had a hard time keeping up with his great creativity.

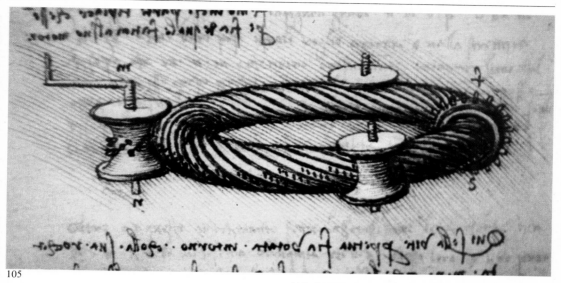

105

105. PERPETUAL SCREW Cod. Madrid I, f.70r.

106. ELEVATOR Cod. Madrid I, f.44r.

107. CHAINS Cod. Atl. f.357r.a.

106

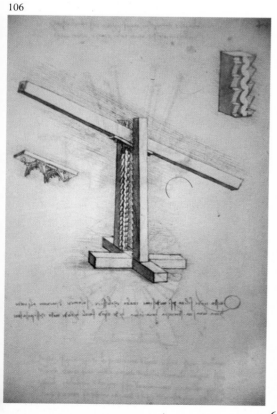

107

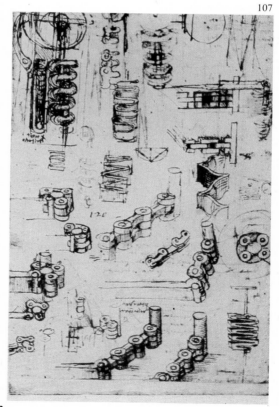

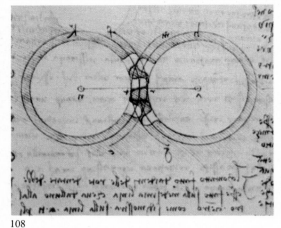

108

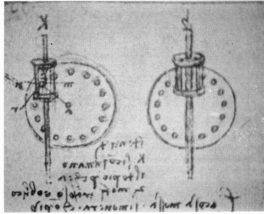

109

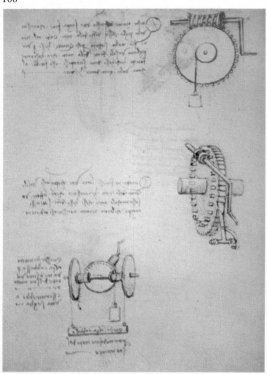

110

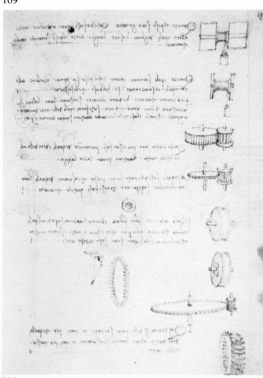

111

108. COG WHEELS Cod. Madrid I, f.5r.

**109. COG WHEEL - LANTERN ROCHET MECHA-
NISM Ms. H, f.86v.**

**110. HELICOIDAL MECHANISM Cod. Madrid I,
f.17v.**

111. GEARS Cod. Madrid I, f.13r.

These are the systems for transmitting motion which appear most often in Leonardo's machines. In order to transmit rotatory move-ment he frequently uses the cogwheel whose cogs' profiles are described geometrically here. To transmit vehicular movement he uses the "cog wheel - lantern rochet" combination in particular, though he warns us that when dealing with great weights or when the axles do not coincide, as in this case, «... *the cogs on K will wear down twice as fast because they have two movements, transverse and oblique*»

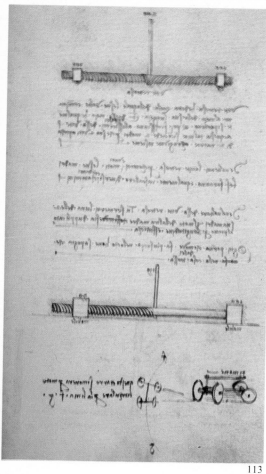

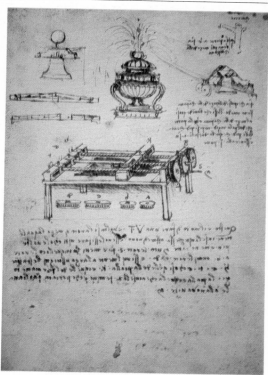

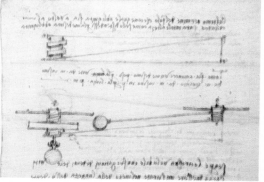

113

112

114

the helicoidal mechanism is preferable (created by the "endless screw" - cog wheel combination) since it's safer and stronger because it "catches many of the wheel's cogs" thus distributing the force. In fig. 111 there is a page full of beautiful drawings of gears and motor transmissions.

112. MACHINE FOR THREADING SCREWS Ms. B, f.70v.

113. "RETROSA" SCREW Cod. Madrid I, f.58r.

114. STUDY ON THE SCREW'S TRACTION POWER Cod. Madrid I, f.86v.

The screw plays a very important role in Vincian mechanics and appears in many of his machines. One of his favorite devices combines a left-handed and a right-handed thread on the same stem: it is the so-called "retrosa" screw (fig. 113) used for special effects. In fig.

114 there is a study of the force needed to lift weights with a screw system a compared that needed with an inclined plane.

Such an intense interest had to lead to the creation of a machine for producing screws like the one we see in fig. 112. The crank runs, using gears, the two outer stems (which have already been thread) that the cutter (K) runs on, homogeneously threading the stem in the middle. Under the bench there are gears of various sizes that can be substituted according to the desired pitch.

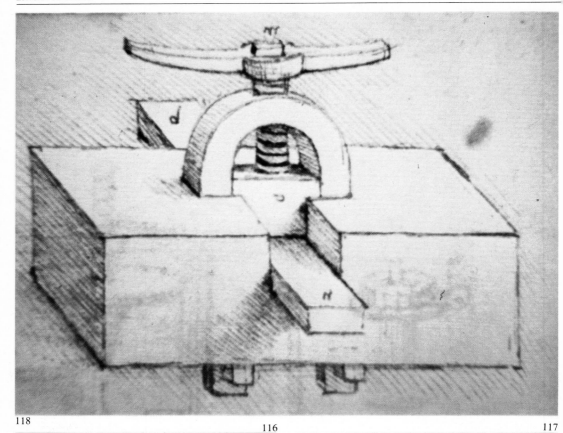

118

117

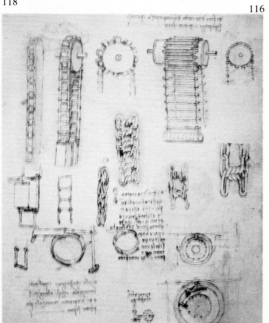

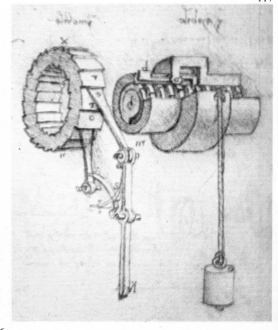

115. PULLEYS Cod. Madrid I, f.87r.
116. CHAINS Cod. Madrid I, f.10r.
117. RATCHET GEARS Cod. Madrid I, f.12r.

Another way to transmit motion is to use pulleys: wheels with grooves which rotate around their own axes and which are connected with cords or straps (fig. 115). They are often used by Leonardo in his flying machines.

In fig. 116 we find examples of flexible chains that theoretically could transmit continuous motion. But the square shape of the teeth and the weights hanging on them lead us to believe that they were meant to transmit discontinuous motion and in particular were conceived for release mechanisms like clocks.

The rachet gears shown here in figure 117 can be used in machines for lifting and in those which depend on falling weights for motion.

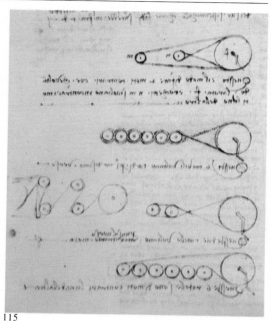

115

119

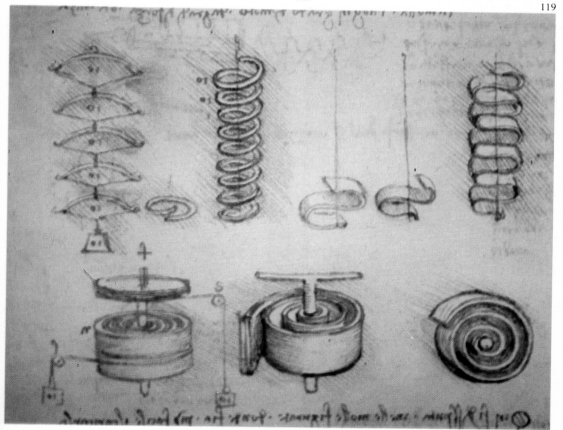

118. MACHINE FOR MAKING SPRINGS Cod. Madrid I, f.14v.

119. SPRINGS Cod. Madrid I, f.85r.

The spring is another energy source that is used especially in devices like clocks or which require little energy. In fig. 119 there is a full set of examples of springs which Leonardo planned to make with a special machine (fig. 118) that he describes as an «... *instrument for making a spring which sets a watch in motion*».

There is a long description of how it works: it simply progressively crushes a transversal rod of metal (nb) using a screw. This process is repeated until the metal «*reaches the thickness of a heavy sheet of paper*» and can be wound into the spring's typical spiral form.

120. BALL BEARINGS Cod. Madrid I, f.20v.

121. BALL AND ROLL BEARINGS Cod. Madrid I, f.101v.

In order to solve the problem of friction in machines (which is directly connected with the problem of transmitting motion) Leonardo devised various systems. In order to bear the thrust of a verticle axle, for example, both ball and roll bearings like the ones in fig. 121 could be used. But the drawing of a bearing with a sliding ring is even more extraordinary. The ring allows the balls to move freely without touching eachother (fig. 120). Leonardo's ball bearing is incredibly modern and foreshadows some of today's solutions. However we musn't forget that rolls and balls had already been used in classical antiquity.

120

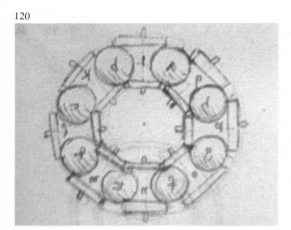

121

122. TRANSFORMATION OF ALTERNATING TO CONTINUOUS MOTION Cod. Atl. f8v.-b.

123. TRANSFORMATION OF CONTINUOUS TO ALTERNATING MOTION Cod. Madrid I, f.29v.

124. TRANSFORMATION OF CONTINUOUS MOTION TO ALTERNATING MOTION Cod. Madrid I, f.30r.

Leonardo's machines often require the transformation of motion as can be seen in the drawings in figures 122, 123, and 124. Fig. 122 is one of Leonardo's most beautiful technical drawings which shows, from right to left, first its individual mechanical parts and then its mechanism completely assembled, a device for lifting weights which exploits the transformation of alternating motion to rotatory or continuous motion. The movement starts with a vertical lever (on the right of the mechanism) which catches the stop cogs as it jerks back and forth (it is drawn inside the crown and in the detail study) and sets in motion the cog wheel which in turn engages the lantern connected to the shaft to which the weight to be lifted is attached.

Instead the figures 123 and 124 show ways to transform circular into alternating motion. The drawing in fig. 123 refers to a textiles machine and shows how to wind a thread evenly around a rochet, starting from the rotatory movement of the crank and using the movement of a connecting-rod which moves back and forth, in and out of the hollow shaft.

122

123

124

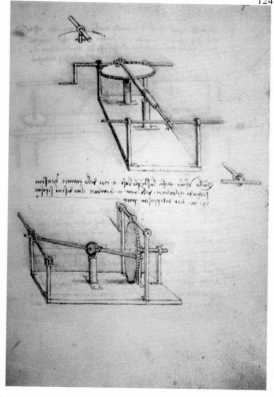

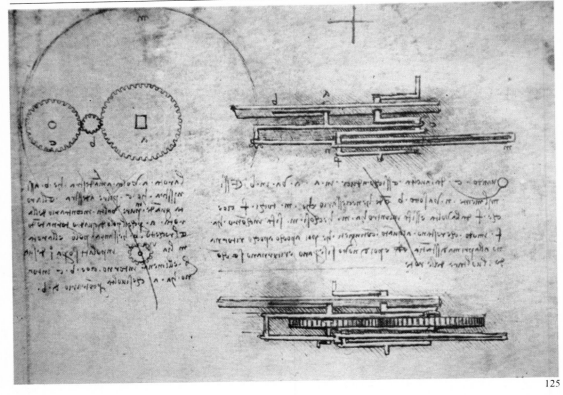

125

125. EPICYCLOIDAL WHEEL MECHANISM
Cod. Atl. f. 27v.-a.

This mechanism is intended for producing the different velocities needed in clocks, in machine tools and in vehicles. It can be related to the gear box studies.

It is made with three cog wheels which are solidly interconnected and arranged along the radius of a bigger wheel called a "planetario". The central wheel is set in motion from within by a crank and transmits its movement to the outer aligned wheel. Only the wheel in the middle is independent from the "planetario" while the other two are solidly connected to it. As the motion of the central wheel is transmitted to the external one, the "planetario" gets turned as well, but it does so at a speed which has been reduced as compared to the initial one. The revolution completed by the outer wheel on its own axis as compared to the circumference of the "planetario" is called an "epicycloidal curve".

126. MACHINES FOR PROCESSING MIRRORS AND LENSES Cod. Atl. f.396v.

Leonardo showed great interest in problems of optics, a science which had become very popular at that time even in the philosophical field. On the page reproduced in figure 126 he drew several machines for producing mirrors and lenses: the second one from the top refers to processing concave mirrors; the third one to grinding them; the fourth one to processing flat mirrors; the first one and the last one enable us to grind and smooth mirrors and lenses simultaneously by transforming rotatory motion to alternating motion.

We also know of a project (made between 1513 and 1516, during his Roman sojourn) for a big parabolic mirror with many facets that was conceived to heat the boilers of a laundry by concentrating solar energy.

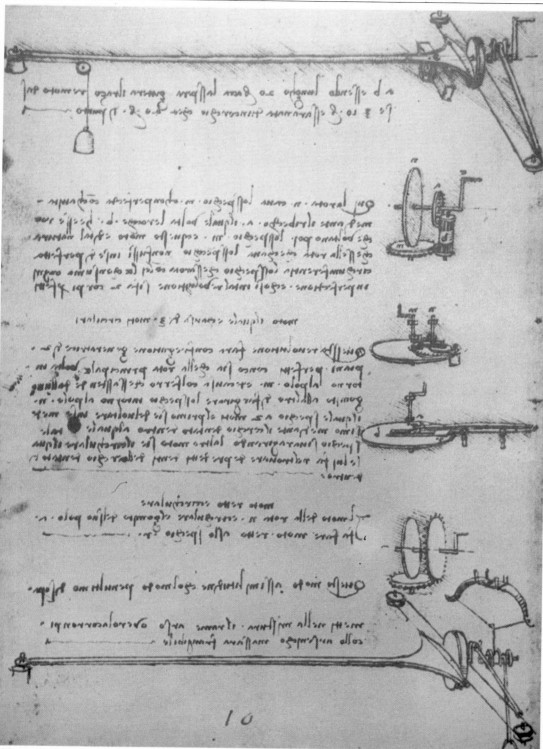

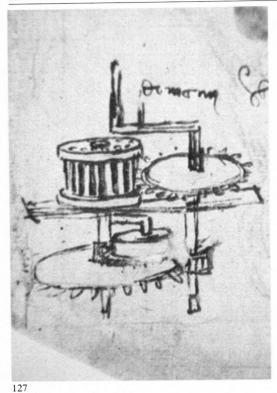

127

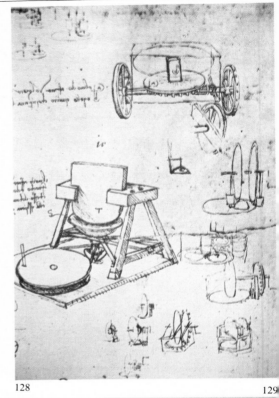

128

129

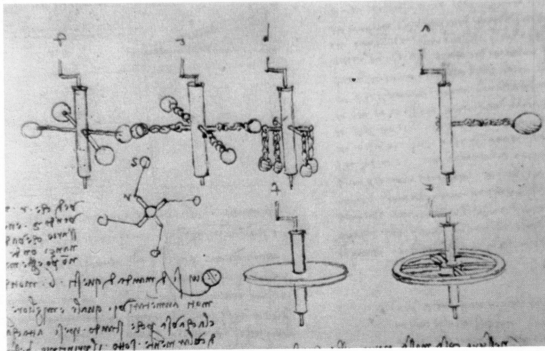

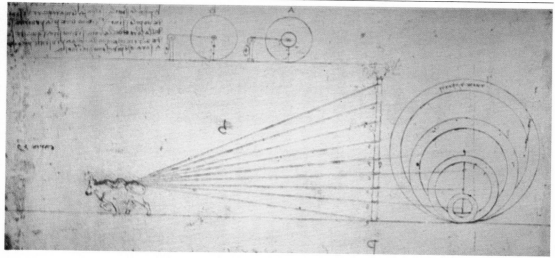

130

127. TRANSMISSION SYSTEM Cod. Atl. f.4v.-b.
128. TRANSMISSION OF MOTION TO AN AXLE Cod. Atl. f.4v.

The drawing at the top of fig. 128 shows how to transmit motion to the axle of a wagon. A crank turns the cog wheel which engages the lantern rochet which is linked to the wagon's axle and which increases its velocity. Motion is transmitted to only one of the wheels so that the other one can move at a different speed when the wagon is rolling. Today the differential serves the same purpose.

129. FLY WHEELS Cod. Madrid I, f.114r.

A fly wheel like the one in the drawing in figure 129, can have either a wheel or weights hung on chains. In any case they are — as Leonardo says — "increasing motions" useful for overcoming points of inertia and for diminishing the strain.

130. STUDIES ON TRACTION Cod. Atl. f.221r.-a.

In this wonderful drawing we see a pair of oxen intent on pulling a wheel which grows geometrically. We draw the conclusion that the force needed to move it diminishes as the diameter of the wheel increases.

131. GEAR SHIFT Cod. Atl. f.27.v.-a.

In fig. 131 we see two rochets (a conical one and a cylindrical one) which transmit motion

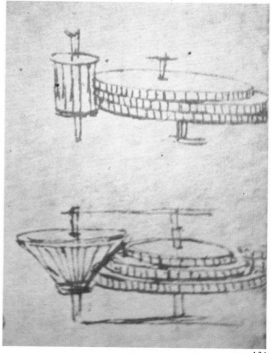

131

to cog wheels with different diameters. Each one has its own velocity that equals the time needed to complete a whole rotation. This system is essentially based on the same principles as the gear shift in modern cars. At Leonardo's time this device could have been used for mills and various types of machinery.

73

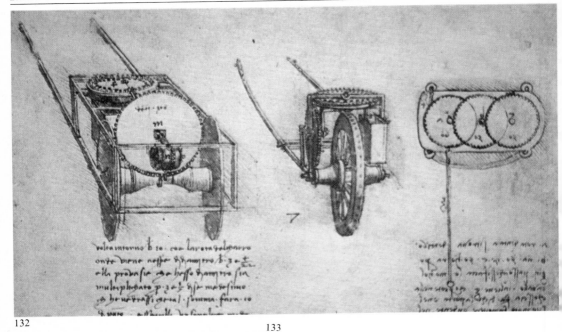

132

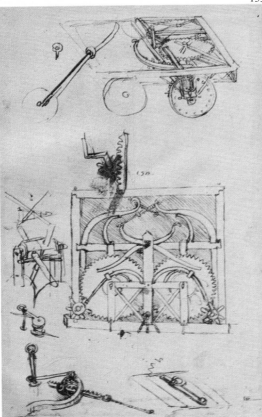

133

132. ODOMETER Cod. Atl. f.1r.

This is a machine for exact distance calcula-tions. It is shaped like a wheelbarrow and has two cog wheels: the vertical one moves one notch each time the hub of the wheel on the ground turns; every time the vertical cog wheel completes a revolution an internal protrusion moves the other, horizontal wheel. This has holes in it, so that it can drop a stone or a ball into a special container each time it moves one notch. By saving and counting these stones one can calculate the number of revolutions of the wheel on the ground and thus measure di-stances.

133. AUTOMOBILE VEHICLE Cod. Atl. f.296v.-a.

This is one of Leonardo's most famous techni cal drawings, especially because it has been considered the forerunner of the modern auto mobile. It is actually a self-propelling wagon whose movement is provided by a complicated crossbow mechanism which when released transmits its energy to the gears linked to the wheel. The rear wheels have differential gear so that they can move independently. A fourth wheel is connected to a kind of rudder which i supposed to guide the wagon. Presumably in tended for court entertainment, this vehicle

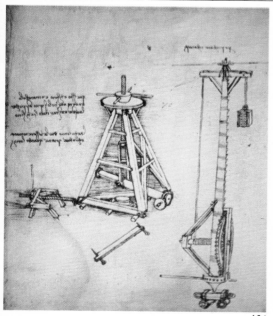

134   135

136

belongs to the same tradition as the automatons and as the self-propelled machines built by other medieval and renaissance engineers.

134. CRANE ON A CART AND SCREW ELEVATOR
Cod. Atl. f.49v.-a.

135. CRANE WITH AN ANNULAR PLATFORM
Cod. Atl. f.295r.-b.

136. MODEL OF A CRANE WITH AN ANNULAR PLATFORM, Museum of Vinci - Ist. Costr. Univ. di Firenze

According to Vasari, when Leonardo was still a boy he designed and imagined many machines for lifting weights including one which was supposed to lift the whole Baptistry of St. John and then replace it on the foundations that would have been built in the meantime.
The incredible undertaking planned by Leonardo has local precedents in the just as incredible project for the dome for which Brunelleschi designed and built special cranes and elevating machines.
Inspired by such a model and by the original Brunelleschian machines, Leonardo designed a few cranes that we show here. Recent studies have revealed that the tall crane mounted on a cart so that it could be moved following a string guide stretched above (fig. 134) could have been used in the dome construction. And

as far as the one on an annular platform is concerned (fig. 135), it had been used by many other architects and engineers at the end of the fourteen hundreds and is probably a copy of the machine used to construct the lantern of S. Maria del Fiore.

75

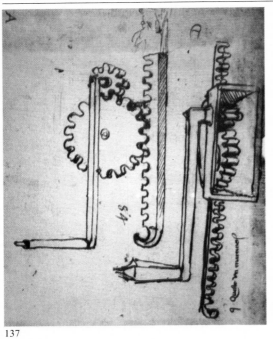

137

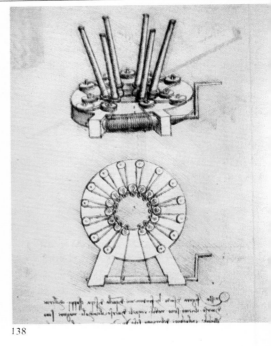

138

139

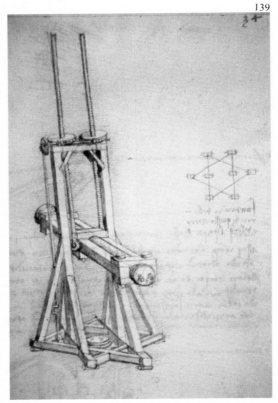

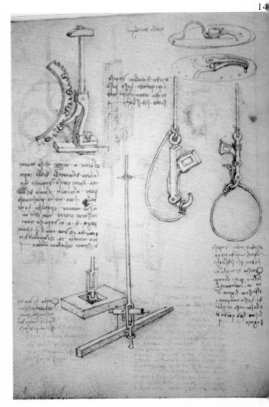

14

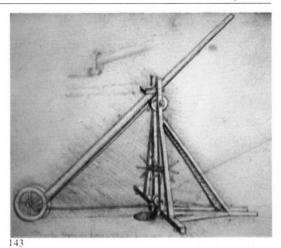

143

37. JACK Cod. Atl. f.539r.

This machine is easy to understand for anyone who has ever tried to change a tire. It is made from a crank, reduction gears and a rod with teeth which moves up and down.

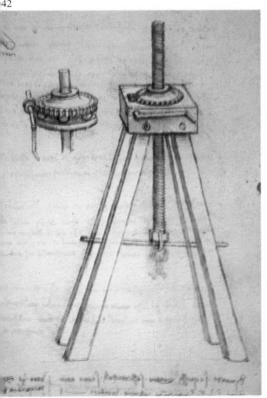

138. MACHINE FOR PULLING Cod. Madrid I, f.44r.

Leonardo shows us the plan and the cross-section of this machine for pulling and also explains how it works: «... *know that the wheels closest to the center are movable, and those towards the larger circle are fixed. And as the winch is turned a circular movement is made so that the inner reels move towards the outer reels and pull that which is attached to them along with them*».

139. DOUBLE JACK SCREW Cod. Madrid I, f.34r.

The double jack screw reproduced in fig. 139 is slow but strong. Operated by the crank on the left it relies on the sure helicoidal system to turn the two long screws upwards synchronously. It is particularly suitable for lifting bulky and heavy objects like columns and cannons.

140. AUTOMATIC RELEASE MECHANISM
   Cod. Madrid I, f.19v.

These are two systems for releasing loads automatically. As long as the loads are hanging the slip knot tightens itself securely and then unties itself thanks to counter weights as it touches the ground.

141. MODEL OF A MACHINE FOR PULLING
   Museum of Vinci (Boldetti)
142. JACK SCREW Cod. Madrid I, f.26r.

Among the machines for lifting weights, the jack screw is particularly strong (fig. 142) and

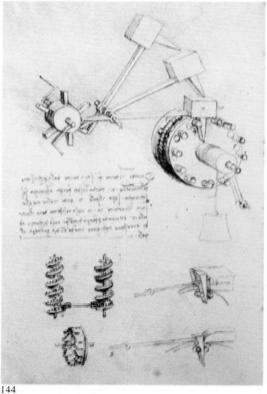

144

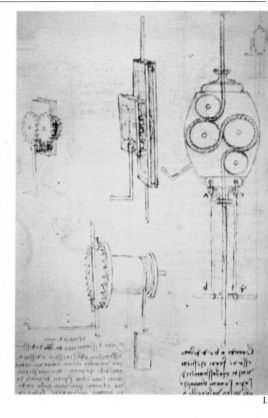

is commanded by a crank and a helicoidal mechanism.

Problems that derive from the friction between the nut which turns and the jack screws plate are brilliantly solved by Leonardo by using ball bearings.

143. MACHINE FOR LIFTING CONSIDERABLY LONG OBJECTS Cod. Madrid I, f.43r.

«...*Moving any weight is easier in a straight line than in an oblique line*...»: from this assumption springs the machine in fig. 143 used for lifting poles or columns. A rope connected to a winch pulls the object to be lifted horizontally from the base, diminishing the effort considerably; even the wheels help by limiting the strain. The drawing and the comment should be connected with Leonardo's interest in geometry and in this particular case for the triangle.

144. HAMMER LIFT Cod. Madrid I, f.92v.

Once again for lifting weights Leonardo designed a hammer system which works «*by means of blows, like in coining*» on a cog wheel.

Blow after blow of the three parallel hammers turns the wheel and the drum to which the weight is attached.

145. CRANK ELEVATOR Cod. Madrid I, f.9r.

It's made of four wheels, two of which drive while two are free: between the latter there is a rope wound in a figure 8. The mechanism is set in motion by a crank which operates one of the cog wheels. There are also iron connecting rods which end in a stirrup-foot rest. A person with his feet on this support and tied with a belt, can go up and down the rope along with the whole mechanism by turning the crank.

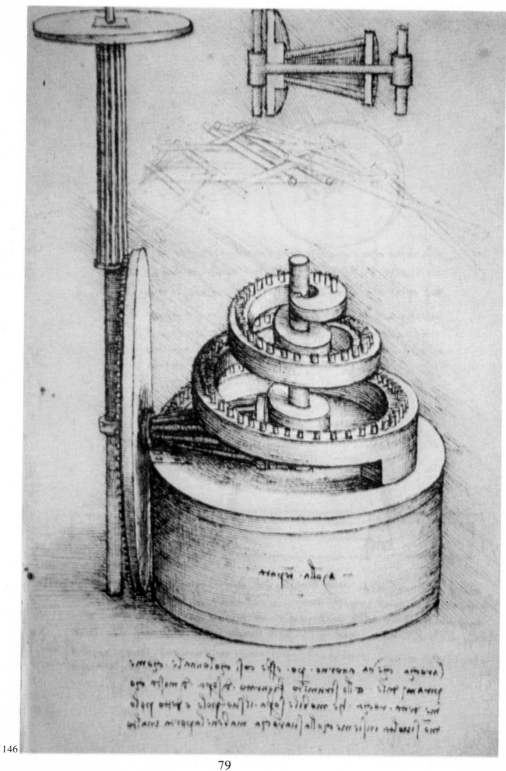

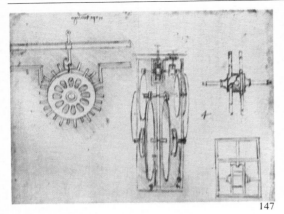

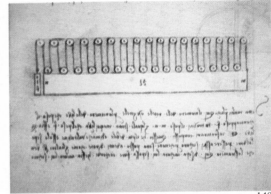

147

148

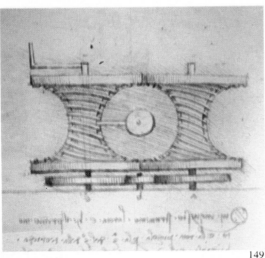

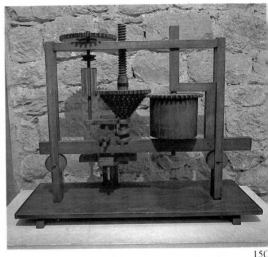

149

150

146. CLOCK MECHANISM
  Cod. Madrid I, f.45r.
147. CLOCK MECHANISM
  Cod. Atl. f.348v.-a.
148. CLOCK MECHANISM
  Cod. Madrid I, f.36v.
149. CLOCK MECHANISM
  Cod. Madrid I, f.18v.
150. MODEL OF A CLOCK MECHANISM
  Museum of Vinci (Boldetti)
151. CLOCK MECHANISM
  Cod. Madrid I, f.14r.
152. CLOCK MECHANISM
  Cod. Madrid I, f.27r.
153. CHIARAVALLE CLOCK
  Cod. Atl. f.399v.-b.

Leonardo was quite interested in clock mechanisms and in anything that had to do with measuring time. Even scanning the Codex Atlanticus we could sense his assiduous interest and when the Codices in Madrid were rediscovered we not only found further proof of it but also recovered some of Leonardo's most beautiful drawings. In northern Italy there was a pre-existing tradition of clock work and there were already many public clocks in Leonardo's times. For example we can cite the famous "Chiaravalle clock" on the tower of the abbey near Milan which according to Leonardo «...*shows the moon, the sun, the hours and the minutes*». The study of this clock's mechanisms (fig. 153) — together with the drawing in fig. 147 which seems to have been sketched from a well known XIV century French clock — probably represent his first fundamental steps in the field of clock work. Once he was introduced to the subject, Leonardo proceeded with variations and improvements: clocks with weights, for example, which are the forerun

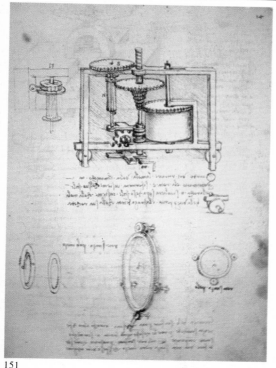

151

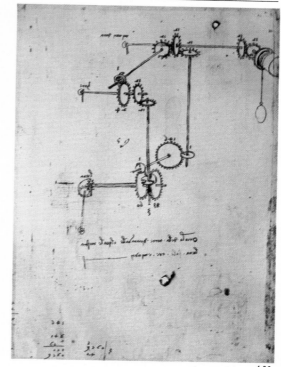

152

153

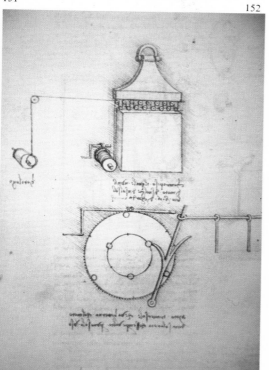

ners of and obtain the same results as those run by springs. They required, however, too much vertical space to stretch themselves out in. Thus he thought out a pulley system that regulated the weight's descent and reduced the vertical space needed (figs. 148 and 152). He also dealt with the problem of how to compensate for the drop in energy which occurs as the spring unwinds: at first he solves it with a spindle which slowly feeds cat gut to the spring, but later he designs extraordinary mechanisms that are more solid and resistant than the spindle. In fig. 151 and in the model in fig. 150 the spring's drum has cogs which engage a conical spiral which in turn moves the spring's drum the distance required by the spiral using a helicoidal device and the rack on the bottom. A variation appears in the drawing in fig. 146 that shows another conical equalizing device linked to the principal spring (inside the box) by means of a rochet which climbs up the conical cog spiral.

In the Madrid Codex there are also other clock mechanisms whose use remains obscure, but which are extremely refined and ingenious both from a graphic point of view and from that of the mechanical intuition (figure 149).

154

DVODECEDRON ELEVA
TVS VACVVS

156

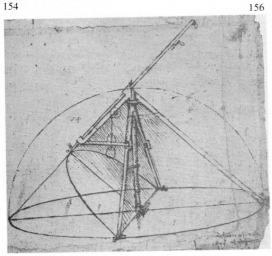

155

156. PARABOLIC COMPASS. Cod. Atl. f.394r.-a

Among the instruments useful for studying
geometry is the compass for tracing a parabola
with a continuous movement which appears in
a drawing from the pages of the Codex Atlanticus. The drawing has no explanation.

157. PROOF OF THE IMPOSSIBILITY
OF PERPETUAL MOTION Cod. Madrid I, f.145r

Leonardo proved the impossibility of perpetual motion, the subject of many discussions
in his time, using drawings and comments.
The instrument drawn here is built from sticks
with weights attached to the ends of them and
the experiment shows Leonardo that, «... no
matter how much weight is attached to the
wheel, which weight will cause its movement
doubtlessly the center of such a weight will
stop at the center of its pole; and no instrument that human genius can invent which
turns on its axis will be able to avoid such an
effect». And thereupon the polemic taunt
«... Oh followers of continuous motion, how
many varied geniuses you have created in such
a research! You belong to the same fold of
those who seek gold [the magician-alche-
mists]».

154. STUDY OF A POLIHEDRON
FOR THE "DE DIVINA PROPORTIONE"
BY L. PACIOLI

155. PLATE XXXII FROM THE
"DE DIVINA PROPORTIONE" BY L. PACIOLI

Leonardo's interest in geometry grew upon his
acquaintance with the Franciscan mathematician Luca Pacioli who was in Milan from
1496. The friendship became so intense that
Leonardo drew with «... his ineffable left
hand...» — as Pacioli calls it — «... The five
regular figures...» which illustrated the lost
edition of "De Divina Proportione" by the
friar. The "regular figures" were first mentioned by Plato and symbolize the Universe's
geometry.

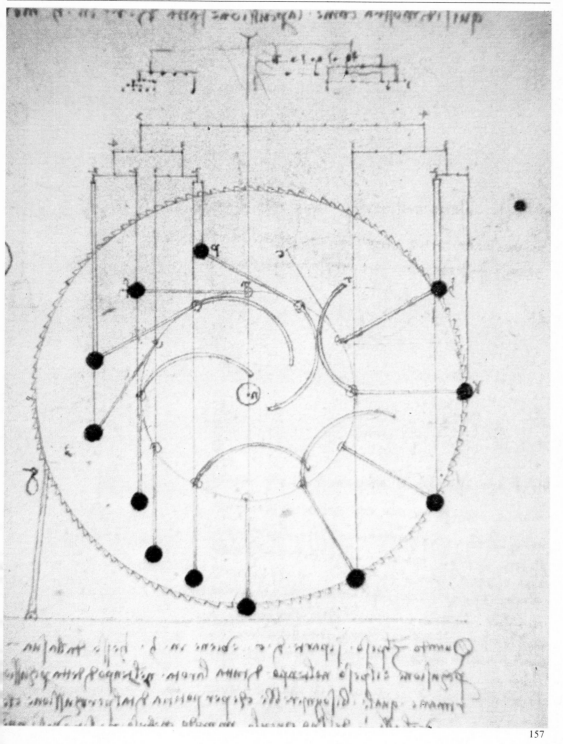

157

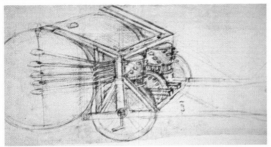

158

161

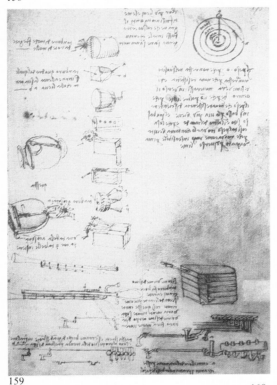

159

160

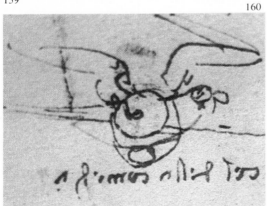

158. MILITARY DRUM Cod. Atl. f.306v.-a
159. WIND INSTRUMENTS Cod. Arundel f.175r.
160. "OCEL DE LA COMEDIA" Cod. Atl. f.231v.-a
161. ROTATING MOUNTAIN Cod. Arundel f.224r.

In Milan Leonardo created scenography. The most famous set is still the one made in 1490 for the marriage of G. Galeazzo Sforza and Isabella d'Aragona known as the "Festa del Paradiso" (Heavenly Celebration); later he produced many other performances including Poliziano's "Orfeo" to which the drawing in figure 161 refers. It is the project for a movable set with a series of counterweight mechanisms that open the mountain during the performance.

We would also like to mention Leonardo's automatons: these are mechanical animals like the lion with a chest full of lilies which opened for Francis I of France (no drawing for it has survived) and "l'ocel de la comedia" (the bird of comedy) shown here in fig. 160. We musn't forget that complex mechanical scenography full of special effects and coups de théâtre have famous precedents in the Brunelleschian tradition.

Leonardo also applies his creativity to the musical field which he considers second only to painting among the arts. The sources speak of his abilities as a lute player and tell us that he was received by Ludovico il Moro for the first time in 1482 holding a silver one. And music also plays a role in Leonardo's major scenographies to which the instruments in figure 159 are probably related. Another field where he

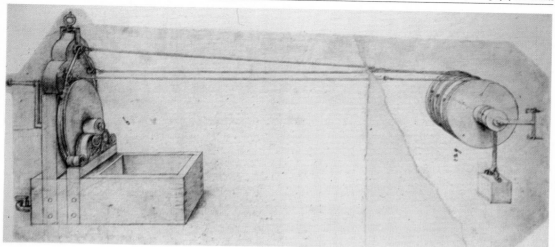

162

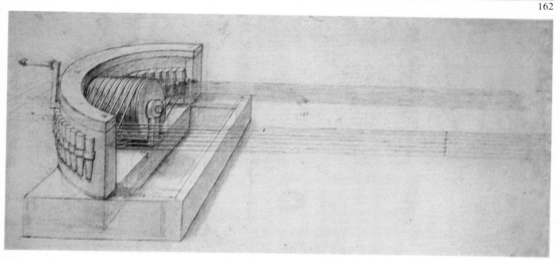

163

uses music is in battle with mechanized military drums which play complicated rhythms according to the movements of the wagon's axle (fig. 158).

162. MACHINE FOR TWISTING ROPES
  Cod. Atl. f.2v.

163. MACHINE FOR TWISTING ROPES
  Cod. Atl. f.2v.-b

164. FIN SPINDLE Cod. Atl. f.393v.-a

165. MACHINE FOR SPINNING BOBBINS
  Cod. Madrid.I, f.65v.

166. MODEL OF A TEXTILES MACHINE
  Museum of Vinci (Boldetti)

Textiles have always been an important indu-

stry both in Tuscany and in Lombardy. Leonardo applied his energies to this field studying machines for spinning, for twisting ropes, for finishing cloth, etc. In order to make a rope, for example, one must twist some strands together (each made of several single threads): Leonardo designed a machine with a crank movement which, using pulleys, can turn the rochets to which the strands to be twisted are attached. In figure 162 there are only three strands, but in the case of the machine in figure 163 there are many more of them arranged in a semi-circle around the drum on which the pulleys wind themselves. His real innovation in the spinning field lies in the fin spindle (fig. 164) which allows the machine to stretch,

85

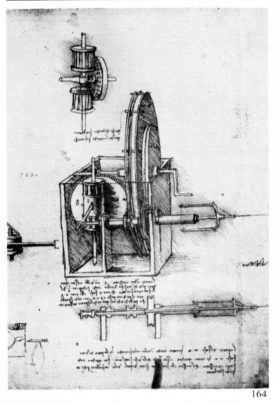

164

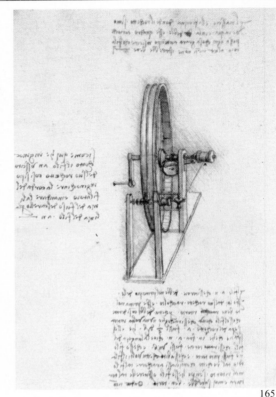

165

twist and spool at the same time at three different points of the same thread. The spindle and the fin move simultaneously but each of them make a different number of rotations. The fin twists the thread and permits the spooling by rotating more rapidly than the spindle. The spindle is also subject to an alternating motion as well to the rotation. It "comes and goes" allowing the thread to wind in regular spirals over the whole length of the spool. For this operation Leonardo designed a special machine separately (fig. 165) whose movement can be seen in detail in figure 123 and in the model in fig. 166.

166

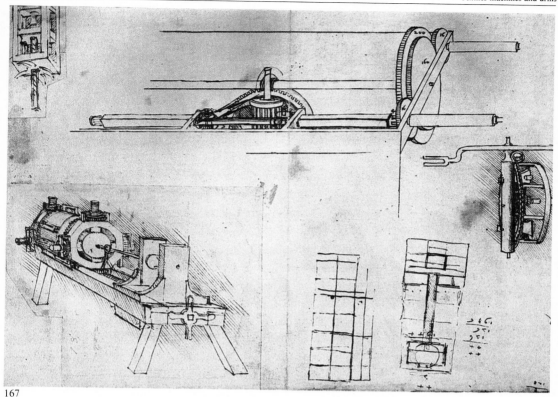

167

168

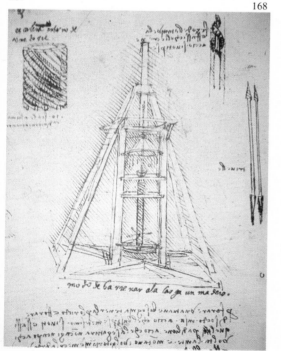

167. HORIZONTAL DRILL Cod. Atl. f.393r.

While quite similar to modern lathes the machine at lower left in figure 167 is actually a horizontal drill for boring the trunks used as water ducts. The innovation consists in the possibility of regulating, with a series of mandrels, the position of the trunk so that its center is aligned with the drill.

168. VERTICAL DRILL Ms. B. f.47v.

Once again the drill in figure 168 is intended for boring trunks: the device operates from the bottom upwards by means of a screw pushed by the men who walk on the platform; between the trunk and the screw there is a kind of upside-down funnel which prevents the sawdust from falling on the workmen's heads.

modo che la lima finisca fino p lui motor fino

169

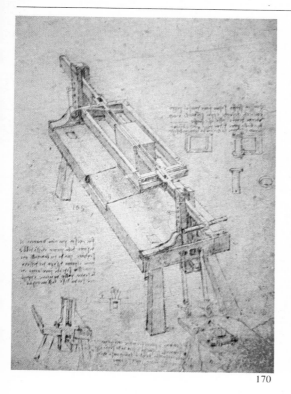

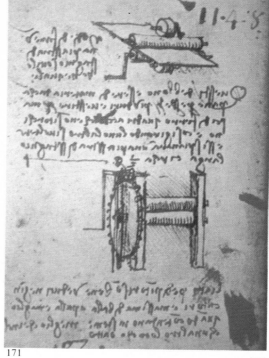

170   171

172

169. MACHINE FOR CUTTING FILES
Cod. Atl. f.6r.-b

Both the drawing's beauty and the ingeniou-
ness of the mechanics make this file cutting
machine very interesting. The operation is
completely automatic: the weight falls unwinding the rope and activating both the rise and
the fall of the hammer and the progress of the
piece to be cut, by using gears and levers. The
complete automatiom not only helps Man but
also gives more homogeneous results, foresha-
dowing modern production processes.

170. MACHINE FOR CUTTING STONES
Cod. Atl. f.1r.-c

On the drawing of the stone cutting machine,
which is extremely beautiful, Leonardo comments: «*the saw movement must go on long
enough to allow the saw's center of gravity to
reach the ends of the stone being cut and
what's more, so that the saw is pulled up on
the slightest side in order to leave room for the
insertion of the emery which fits under the
lifted part of the saw...*».

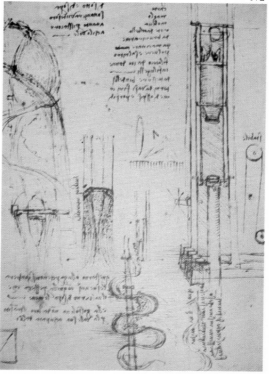

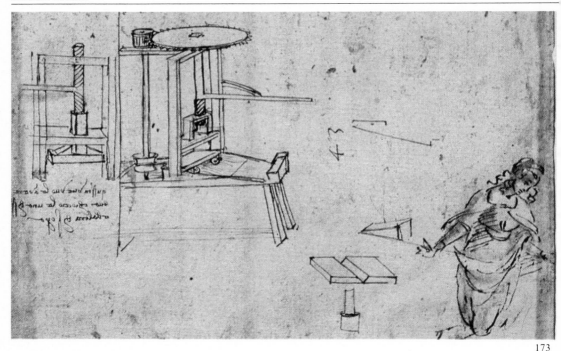

173

171. ROLLING-MILL Ms. I f.48v.

There are many devices that Leonardo uses to shape metals. In fig. 171 we see two machines for producing sheets of tin by making the metal pass between the principal rollers. In the sketch on the top there is, however, an important addition: two smaller rollers which keep up the pressure on the principal ones so that the sheet produced is homogeneously smooth.

172. PILE DRIVER Cod. Atl. f.289r.

The driving weight is lifted by a winch and is released automatically at the maximum height in order to drive the pile which it deep into hits the ground. The operation, which is simple and not particularly tiring, can be repeated many times until the pile has been driven to the desired depth. This machine is particularly useful when driving the piles for a hydraulic basin.

173. PRINTING PRESS Cod. Atl. f.358r.

Printing was invented in Leonardo's lifetime and he contributes to the process's improvement with a variety of solutions like the one in the drawing in figure 173, where we see a press

(with a type-bearing boogie which slides on wheels) which automatically returns to the printing position thanks to a gear and rope system. Normally the operation had to be done manually, requiring more time and energy. Paradoxically none of Leonardo's written works were published until the XVII century.

174. FLOODLIGHT Cod. Atl. f.9v.-b

It is simply a box with a large glass lens on one side and a candle inside: this is how Leonardo made «*an intense and wide light*». The principle is the same one used in floodlights and we believe that the idea is related to scenographic needs.

174

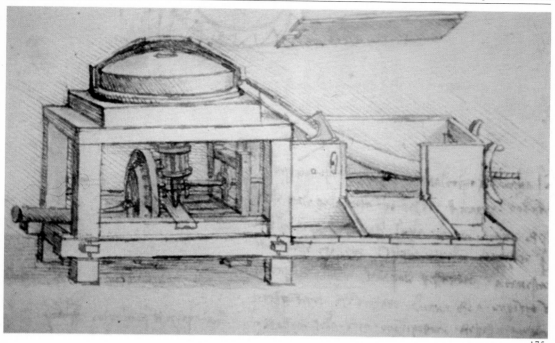

175

drawing in figure 175 Leonardo designs a strange machine for grinding grain which falls down a slide into a cloth sleeve (see fig. 176); this then gets shaken with a pole that is connected to the gears of the milling wheel so that the flour can escape from the cloth separating itself from the bran.

177. OIL PRESS Cod. Atl. f.14r.a

Leonardo dedicated many studies to agricultural techniques and to machines for processing soil and its products. The oil press, which belongs to the Tuscan agricultural traditions, represents an example of the most elementary technological applications (of counter weights and wheel mechanisms) for aiding and saving manual labour.

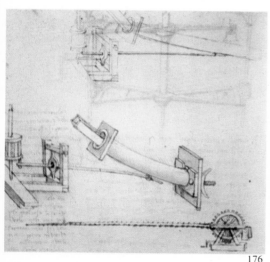

176

175. MACHINE FOR SEPARATING BRAN FROM FLOUR Cod. Madrid I, f.22r.

176. MACHINE FOR SEPARATING BRAN FROM FLOUR (internal mechanisms) Cod. Madrid I, f.21v.

Leonardo also tried to improve the techniques for milling grain and there are many drawings of mills which make more efficient use of the water's course or which can follow the wind's direction since they have movable roofs. In the

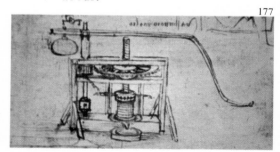

177

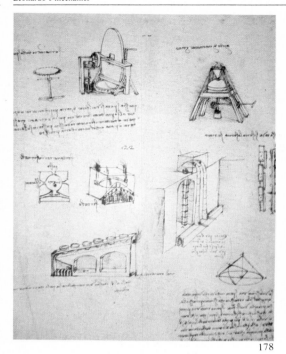

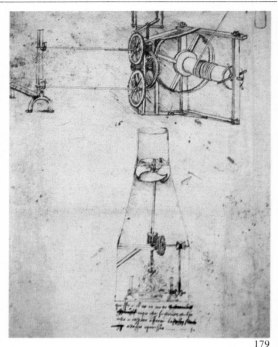

178

179

178. REFLEX OVEN Cod. Atl. f.396r.-e

In connection with the art of foundry Leonardo designed many ovens and here we publish a "reflex" oven where the flame doesn't heat the materials to be melted directly; instead, the heat reflected by the walls liquefies the metal.

179. AUTOMATIC ROASTING-JACK Cod. Atl. f.5v.

The automatic rosting-jack is very interesting because it make rare use of hot air as an energy source. As this rises it sets the blades in motion, which in turn engage the pole on the right, on the end of which there is a pulley which turns the spit. It is all entirely automatic, including the regulation of the speed of the spit which turns faster or slower according to the size of the fire.

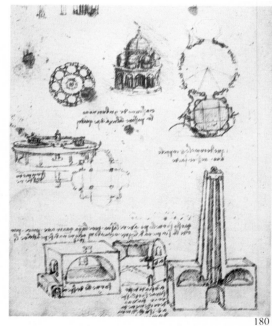

180

180. STUDY OF OVENS AND OF ARCHITECTURE Ms. B. f.21v.

181. MODEL OF AN ELEVATING MACHINE, Museum of Vinci - Ist. Costr. Univ. Firenze

182. MODEL OF A JACK-SCREW, Museum of Vinci (Boldetti), see fig. 142.

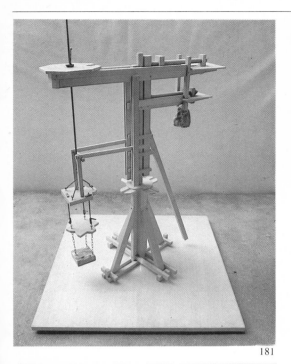

183

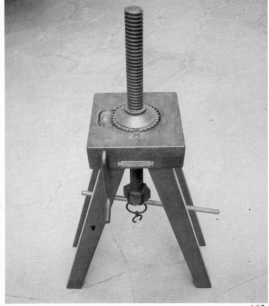

181

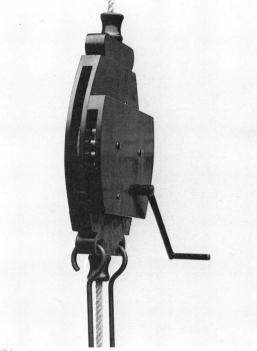

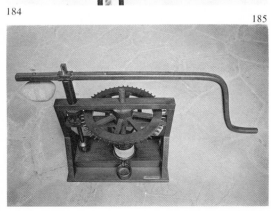

182

184

185

183. MODEL OF AN ESCAVATING MACHINE,
Museum of Milan

184. MODEL OF A CRANK ELEVATOR,
Museum of Vinci (Boldetti), see fig. 145

185. MODEL OF AN OIL PRESS, Museum of Vinci
(Boldetti), see fig. 177

1452 - During the night of April 15 Leonardo is born in Vinci, the "illegitimate" son of Ser Piero, a notary, and of Catherine; he passed all of his childhood in Vinci and its outskirts and between 1466 and 1469 followed his father to Florence where he bound as an apprentice in Verrocchio's workshop;

1473 - the first dated drawing (August 5) and, in these years, works in paint like the angel in Verrocchio's "Baptism" and the "Annunciation" (both in the Uffizi Gallery in Florence);

1481 - he receives the commission for the "Adoration of the Magi" from the friars of S. Donato a Scopeto; the work (kept in the Uffizi) was never finished;

1482 - Leonardo goes to the court of Ludovico il Moro in Milan were he remains until 1499;

1483 - he begins to paint the "Virgin of the Rocks" (Paris, Louvre);

1495 - he paints the "Last Supper" in S. Maria delle Grazie, in Milan;

1496 - fiendship and collaboration with the mathematician Luca Pacioli;

1499 - with the fall of Ludovico il Moro Leonardo leaves Milan;

1500 - he stays at first in Mantua, then in Venice and finally in Florence;

1502 - he is employed by Cesare Borgia as architect and military engineer; he travels with Borgia and with Machiavelli in Romagna;

1503 - he returns to Florence and starts working on the "Battle of Anghiari" in the Room of the Five Hundred in Palazzo Vecchio;

1504 - he paints the "Mona Lisa" (Paris, Louvre). Ser Piero, his father dies. Brief trip of Leonardo to Piombino;

1506 - brief sojourns in Florence and Milan until, in 1508, he settles in the Lombard capi al, for a period of five years on a salary from Louis XII, the King of France;

1509 - he paints the "Saint Anne" (Paris, Louvre);

1513 - he leaves Milan, passes through Florence, and settles for three years in Rome under the patronage of Giuliano dei Medici;

1516 - from Rome Leonardo goes to France with his disciple Francesco Melzi; until his death he will be under the patronage of the King Francis I;

1519 - on May 2 Leonardo dies in Clos Lucé near the castle of Amboise on the Loire, and is buried there in the church of S. Florentin.

BIBLIOGRAPHICAL INDICATIONS

VARIOUS AUTHORS, *Leonardo da Vinci*, Novara, 1956.

CANESTRINI, G., *Leonardo costruttore di macchine e veicoli*, Milano, 1939.

CIANCHI, R., *Il Museo vinciano,* unpublished manuscript 1957.

DE TONI, G., *Studio di meccanica*, in *Leonardo da Vinci*, atti del "Simposio Internazionale di Storia della Scineza", Firenze 1969.

GARIN, E., *La cultura fiorentina nell'età di Leonardo* and *Universalità di Leonardo*, in *Scienza e vita civile nel Rinascimento italiano*, Bari, 1965.

GIACOMELLI, R., *L.d.V. e il problema del volo*, in "Sapere", 1938.

GIACOMELLI, R., *L.d.V. aerodinamico, aerologo, aerotecnico ed osservatore del volo degli uccelli*, in *Atti del Convegno di Studi Vinciani*, Firenze, 1953.

GIBBS-SMITH, C., *Le invenzioni di L.d.V.*, Milano, 1979.

GILLE, B., *Leonardo e gli ingegneri del Rinascimento*, Milano 1972.

MARINONI, A., [edited by], *L.d.V., Scritti Letterari*, Milano 1974.

PEDRETTI, C., *Leonardo architetto*, Milano, 1978.

RETI, L., [edited by] *Leonardo* [essays by S.A. Bedini, A.M. Brizio, M.V. Brugnoli, A. Chastel, B. Dibner, L.H. Heydenreich, A. Marinoni, L. Reti, E. Winternitz, C. Zammattio], Milano, 1974.

RETI, L., *Tracce dei progetti perduti di F. Brunelleschi nel Codice Atlantico di L.d.V.*, in "L.d.V. letto e commentato", Letture Vinciane, Firenze, 1974.

ROSSI, P., *I filosofi e le macchine (1400-1700)*, Milano, 1971.

STEINITZ, J.T., *Leonardo architetto teatrale e organizzatore di feste...*, in "L.d.V. letto e commentato...", Letture Vinciane, Firenze, 1974.

STROBINO, G., *Leonardo da Vinci e la meccanica tessile*, Milano, 1953.

TURSINI, L., *Leonardo e l'arte militare*, in "Rivista d'ingegneria", n. 10, ottobre 1951.

TURSINI, L., *Navi e scafandri negli studi di Leonardo*, in *Leonardo. Saggi e Ricerche*, Roma, 1954.

UCCELLI, A., [edited by] *I libri del volo di Leonardo da Vinci*, Milano, 1952.

UCCELLI, A., [edited by] *I libri di meccanica di L.d.V.*, Milano 1940.

INDICE